Contents

Introduction

About this guide

This unit guide is one of a series covering the Edexcel specification for AS and A2 chemistry. It offers advice for the effective study of **Unit 6B: Synoptic**. Its aim is to help you *understand* the chemistry — it is not intended as a shopping-list, enabling you to cram for an examination. The guide has three sections.

- **Introduction** — this provides guidance on study and revision, together with advice on approaches and techniques to ensure you answer the examination questions in the best way that you can.
- **Content Guidance** — this section is not intended to be a textbook. It offers guidelines on the main features of the content of Unit 6B, together with particular advice on making study more productive. It also contains a number of worked examples.
- **Questions and Answers** — this contains three Unit 6B question papers and some synoptic-style questions. Answers are provided; in some cases, distinction is made between responses that might have been given by a grade-A candidate and those typical of a grade-C candidate. Careful consideration of these will improve your answers and, much more importantly, will improve your understanding of the chemistry involved.

The effective understanding of chemistry requires time. No-one suggests it is an easy subject, but even those who find it difficult can overcome their problems by the proper investment of time.

To understand the chemistry, you have to make links between the various topics. The subject is coherent; it is not a collection of discrete modules. These links only come with experience, which means time spent thinking about chemistry, working with it and solving chemical problems. Time produces fluency with the ideas. If you have that, together with good technique, the examination will look after itself.

The specification

The specification states the chemistry that can be used in the unit tests and describes the format of those tests. This is not necessarily the same as what teachers might choose to teach or what you might choose to learn.

The purpose of this book is to help you with Unit Test 6B, but don't forget that what you are doing is learning *chemistry*. The specification can be obtained from Edexcel, either as a printed document or from the web at **www.edexcel.org.uk**.

The unit test

Command terms

Examiners use certain words that require you to respond in a specific way. You must distinguish between these terms and understand exactly what each requires you to do.

- **Define** — give a simple definition without any explanation
- **Identify** — give the name or formula of the substance
- **State** — no explanation is required (nor should you give one)
- **Deduce** — use the information supplied in the question to work out your answer
- **Suggest** — use your knowledge and understanding of similar substances or those with the same functional groups to work out the answer
- **Compare** — make a statement about *both* substances being compared
- **Explain** — use chemical theories or principles to say why a particular property is as it is
- **Predict** — say what you think will happen on the basis of the principles that you have learned

Calculations

You must show your working in order to score full marks. Be careful about significant figures. If a question does not specify the number of significant figures required, give your answer to *three significant figures* or to two decimal places for pH calculations.

Organic formulae

- **Structural formula** — you must give a structure that is unambiguous. For instance, $CH_3CH_2CH_2OH$ is acceptable, but C_3H_7OH could be either propan-1-ol or propan-2-ol and so is not acceptable. If a compound has a double bond, then it should be shown in the structural formula.
- **Full structural formula** — you must show all the *atoms* and all the *bonds*. 'Sticks' instead of hydrogen atoms will lose marks.
- **Shape** — if the molecule or ion is pyramidal, tetrahedral or octahedral you must make sure that your diagram looks three-dimensional. To do this, use wedges and dashes. Draw optical isomers as mirror images of each other. Geometric isomers must be drawn with bond angles of 120°. Make sure that the *bonds go to the correct atoms*, for example the oxygen in an –OH group or the carbon in $–CH_3$ and –COOH groups.

Points to watch

- **Stable** — if you use this word, you must qualify it; for example: 'stable to heat'; 'the reaction is thermodynamically stable'; 'the reaction is kinetically stable'; or 'a secondary carbocation intermediate is more stable than a primary carbocation'.

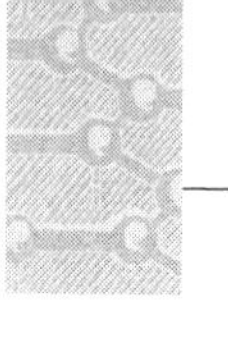

- **Reagents** — if you are asked to identify a reagent, you must give its *full* name or formula. Phrases such as 'acidified dichromate(VI)' will not score full marks. You must identify the acid used and give the reagent's full name, for example 'potassium dichromate(VI)'.
- **Conditions** — the word 'reflux' does not imply heating. If heat is needed, you must say so, i.e. 'heat under reflux'. Don't use abbreviations such as 'hur'.
- **Atoms, molecules and ions** — don't use these words randomly. Ionic compounds contain ions, not molecules.
- **Rules** — don't use rules such as Markovnikov or Le Chatelier to *explain*. However, they can be used to predict.
- **Melting and boiling** — when a molecular covalent substance (such as water) is melted or boiled, *covalent* bonds are *not* broken. So melting and boiling points are connected with the type and strength of *intermolecular* forces. When an ionic substance is melted, the ionic bonds are *not* broken — the substance is still ionic. The ions gain enough energy to separate.

Learning to learn

Learning is not instinctive — you have to develop suitable techniques to make good use of your time. In particular, chemistry has peculiar difficulties that need to be understood if your studies are to be effective from the start.

Planning

Busy people do not achieve what they do haphazardly. They plan — so that if they are working they mean to be working, and if they are watching television they have planned to do so. Planning is essential. You must know what you have to do each day and each week and set aside time to do it.

Be realistic in your planning. You cannot work all the time, so you must build in time for recreation and family responsibilities.

Targets

When devising your plan, have a target for each study period. This might be a particular section of the specification, or it might be rearranging of information from text into pictures, or the construction of a flowchart relating all the organic reactions you need to know. Whatever it is, be determined to master your target material before you leave it.

Reading chemistry textbooks

Chemistry textbooks are a valuable resource, not only for finding out the information for your homework but also to help you understand concepts of which you are unsure. They need to be read carefully, with a pen and paper to hand for jotting down things as you go — for example, making notes, writing equations, doing calculations and drawing diagrams. Reading and revising are *active* processes which require concentration. Looking vaguely at the pages is a waste of time. In order to become fluent and confident in chemistry, you need to master detail.

Chemical equations

Equations are quantitative, concise and internationally understood.

When you write an equation, check that:

- you have thought of the *type* of reaction occurring — for example, is it neutralisation, addition or disproportionation?
- you have written the correct formulae for all the substances
- your equation balances in terms of both the numbers of atoms of each element and the charge
- you have not written something silly, such as having a strong acid as a product when one of the reactants is an alkali
- you have included *state symbols* if they have been asked for and also in all thermochemical equations

Graphs

Graphs give a lot of information, and they must be understood in detail rather than as a general impression. Take time over them. Note what the axes are, the units, the shape of the graph and what the shape means in chemical terms. Think about what could be calculated from the graph. Note if the graph flattens off and what that means. This is especially important in kinetics.

When drawing a graph, do not join up the points — draw a smooth line (straight or curved) as near as possible to all the points. However, if you are plotting a list, such as the first ionisation energies of the elements, then you do join up the points.

Tables

These are a means of displaying a lot of information. You need to be aware of the table headings and the units of numerical entries. Take time over them. What trends can be seen? How do these relate to chemical properties? Sometimes it can be useful to convert tables of data into graphs. When answering questions, use all the given data.

Diagrams

Diagrams of apparatus should be drawn in section. When you see them, copy them and ask yourself why the apparatus has the features it has. What is the difference between a distillation and a reflux apparatus, for example? When you do practical work, examine each piece of the apparatus closely so that you know both its form and function. Make sure you can draw standard apparatus.

Calculations

Do not take calculations on trust — work through them. First, make certain that you understand the problem, and then that you can follow each step in the solution.

Calculations are not normally structured in A2 as they were in AS. Therefore, you will need to *plan* the procedure for turning the data into an answer.

- Set your calculations out fully, making it clear what you are calculating at each step. Don't round figures up or down during a calculation. Either keep all the numbers on your calculator or write any intermediate answers to four significant figures.
- If you have time, check the accuracy of each step by recalculating it. It is so easy to enter a wrong number into your calculator or to calculate a molar mass incorrectly.
- Finally, check that you have the correct *units* in your answer and that you have given it to an appropriate number of *significant figures* — if in doubt, give it to three.

Notes

Most students keep notes of some sort. Notes can take many forms: they might be permanent or temporary; they might be lists, diagrams or flowcharts. You have to develop your own styles — note the plural. For example, notes that are largely words can often be recast into charts or pictures and this is useful for imprinting the material. The more you rework the material, the clearer it will become.

Whatever form your notes take, they must be organised. Notes that are not indexed or filed properly are useless, as are notes written at enormous length and those written so cryptically that they are unintelligible a month later.

Writing

There is some requirement for extended writing in Unit Test 6B. You need to be able to write concisely and accurately. This requires you to marshal your thoughts properly and needs to be practised during your ordinary learning.

For experimental plans, it is a good idea to write your answer as a series of bullet points. There are no marks specifically for 'communication skills', but if you are not able to communicate your ideas clearly and accurately, you will not score full marks.

Approaching the unit test

The unit test is designed to allow you to show the examiner what you know. Answering questions successfully is not only a matter of knowing the chemistry but is also a matter of technique. In Unit Test 6B, you will have to write your answers in the booklet provided and *not* on the question paper as in the other unit tests. You should start the answer to each question on a new page.

Revision

- Start your revision in plenty of time. Make a list of what you need to do, emphasising the topics that you find most difficult — and draw up a detailed revision plan. Work back from the examination date, ideally leaving an entire week free from fresh revision before that date. Be realistic in your revision plan and then add 25% to the timings because everything takes longer than you think.

- When revising, make a note of difficulties and ask your teacher about them. If you do not make these notes, you will forget to ask.
- Make use of past papers. Similar questions are regularly asked, so if you work through as many past papers and answers as possible, you will be in a strong position to obtain a top grade.
- When you use the Question and Answer section of this guide, make a determined effort to write *your* answers *before* looking at the sample answers and examiner's comments.

The exam

Unit Test 6B examines the content of Units 1–5. The paper has two sections. Section A contains one compulsory question based on experimental results. Section B contains three questions, of which you have to answer two. The time allowed is 1 hour 30 minutes, worth 50 marks. This counts for 20% of the A2 or 10% of the whole A-level marks.

- Read the question. Questions usually change from one examination to the next. A question that looks the same, at a cursory glance, to one that you have seen before usually has significant differences when read carefully. Needless to say, candidates do not receive credit for writing answers to their own questions.
- Be aware of the number of marks available for a given part of a question. This is an excellent indication of the number of points that you need to make.
- If you start a question and then give up on it and answer the remaining two, do not cross out what you have written. The examiner will mark all that you have written and award marks for the best two answers.
- Look for words in **bold** in a question and make sure that you have answered the question fully in terms of those words or phrases. For example, if the question asks you to define a **dative covalent bond**, make sure that you explain the meaning of covalent bond as well as dative.
- Questions in Unit Test 6B will often involve substances or situations that are new to you. This is deliberate and is what makes these questions synoptic. Don't be put off by large organic molecules. They are nothing more than a collection of functional groups which, you may assume, react independently of each other.

Unit Test 6B has one assessment objective, A04. This is referred to as 'synthesis of knowledge, understanding and skills'. You should be able to:

- bring together knowledge, principles and concepts from different areas of chemistry, including experiment and investigation, and apply them in a particular context, expressing ideas clearly and logically and using appropriate specialist vocabulary
- use chemical skills in contexts that bring together different areas of the subject

Synoptic issues

This unit test will be synoptic assessment, which is the explicit drawing together of knowledge, understanding and skills learned in different parts of the A-level course. In Unit Test 6B, the questions draw on the content of the whole specification.

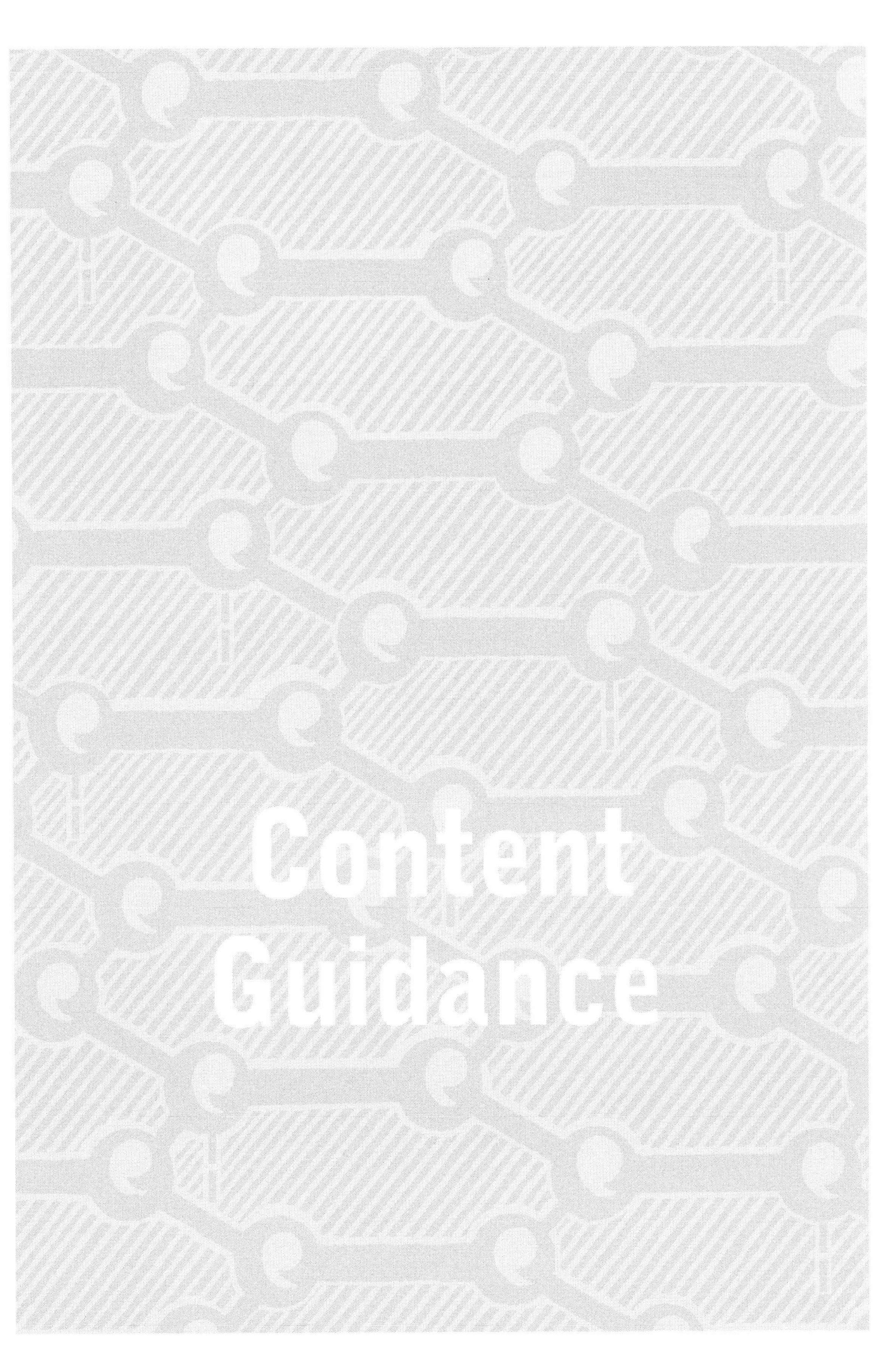

Content Guidance

This section is a guide to the content of **Unit 6B: Synoptic**.

Unit 6B tests the whole AS and A2 specification. However, revising for this unit is not as daunting as it first appears because many AS topics (e.g. energetics, equilibrium, kinetics, redox and organic chemistry) are revisited and further developed at A2, and calculations involving moles occur throughout the course. The topics of Unit 5 should be fresh in your mind, because you will have recently taken the Unit 5 test. However, you will need to revisit the topics in Unit 4 and the work covered in the AS course, particularly bonding, intermolecular forces, shapes of molecules and ions, and empirical formula calculations.

The questions will demand a good understanding of the topics covered by the A-level course, rather than factual recall of reactions and definitions. Unit 6B is the most demanding part of the A-level examination and proper preparation is essential. The grade for Unit 6 is made up of the marks obtained in the written paper, added to those from either the internal assessment of practical skills or the practical examination.

This section is not meant to be a complete revision of the whole specification. It covers some of the more frequently tested topics and some which many students find difficult. A careful study of the text and the worked examples will help you prepare for the exam.

For each part of the specification, you should also consult a standard textbook for more information. Chemistry is a subtle subject, and you need to have a good sense of where the information you are dealing with fits into the larger chemical landscape. This only comes by reading. Remember that the specification tells you only what can be examined in the unit test.

Section A

Section A assesses your ability to interpret data from laboratory situations. The question usually starts with a calculation, possibly based on a reaction you have not met. Don't panic — all the necessary information will be given in the question. However, there are a number of types of calculation that you must be able to perform. The question will then go on to some other chemistry, linked to the compounds in the calculation.

Some examples are set out below. Work your way through these and see if you can do the calculation before looking at the answer given.

Rate of reaction calculations

Initial rate data

In Unit 5, you learned how to use initial rate data to deduce the order of reaction. This could be asked here, but the data will not be quite so straightforward.

Worked example

Use the data below to deduce the partial orders of A and B in the reaction

$A + 2B \longrightarrow C + D$

Experiment	[A]/mol dm^{-3}	[B]/mol dm^{-3}	Initial rate/ mol dm^{-3} s^{-1}
1	0.1	0.1	1.4×10^{-3}
2	0.2	0.1	2.8×10^{-3}
3	0.4	0.2	1.12×10^{-2}

Answer

Comparing experiment 2 with experiment 1: [A] has doubled but [B] has remained the same. The rate has also doubled. Therefore, the order with respect to A is 1.

Comparing experiment 3 with experiment 2: [A] has doubled and [B] has also doubled. The rate has gone up four times because

$$\frac{1.12 \times 10^{-2}}{2.8 \times 10^{-3}} = 4$$

- As the reaction is first order with respect to A, the rate will double because of A, so it must also double because of B.
- Therefore, the reaction is also first order with respect to B.

Tip As the question asks you to *deduce* the orders, you must explain how you work them out. Do this clearly, stating which experiments you are considering, and how the concentrations of *both* reactants have changed.

Concentration–time data

You might be given a graph (or data from which to draw a graph) of concentration plotted against time. There are three likely scenarios.

(1) Calculate the initial rate and the rate at a later time

The rate of reaction is the *gradient* (slope) of the graph. You have to draw a tangent to the graph at time zero to measure the initial rate, and at some other point (e.g. halfway through the reaction) to measure the rate at a later time.

Drawing the graph

If the graph is not drawn on the question paper, you must draw it carefully.

- Draw and label the axes.
- Choose a linear scale that ensures the points, when plotted, use almost all the space.
- Check that you have plotted the points correctly.
- Finally, draw a *smooth* curve through or near to all the points.

Drawing a tangent

- To find the *initial* rate, draw a tangent to the curve where it meets the y-axis, which is at time zero. The tangent must be a straight line and must not cut the graph. The tangent must be at least 3 cm in length. The concentration at time zero is the intercept on the y-axis.
- To find the rate at a different concentration, draw the tangent (again at least 3 cm long) at a second point, so that it *touches* the graph at the chosen concentration but does not cut the graph.

Calculating the gradient and hence the rate

- Carefully measure how much the straight-line tangent changes. This is the difference, Δy, expressed as a positive number, between the two values of the concentration, y, where

  $\Delta y = y_{\text{start}} - y_{\text{at 2nd point}}$
- Then measure the time elapsed, Δx.

  $\Delta x = x_{\text{at 2nd point}} - x_{\text{start}}$
- The gradient, which is the rate of the reaction, equals $\Delta y/\Delta x$.

The example below shows how to calculate the value of $\Delta y/\Delta x$ for a straight line.

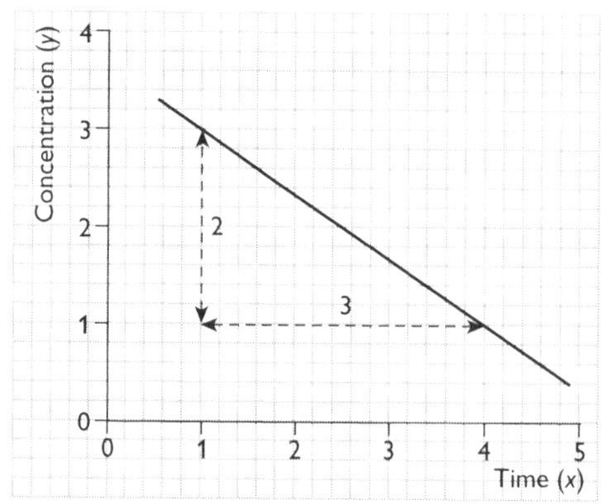

$\Delta y = 3 - 1 = 2$

$\Delta x = 4 - 1 = 3$

The rate of reaction at concentration 3 units

$= \dfrac{\Delta y}{\Delta x} = \dfrac{2}{3} = 0.67$

Worked example

The ester ethyl ethanoate undergoes hydrolysis in alkaline solution.

$$CH_3COOC_2H_5 + OH^- \longrightarrow CH_3COO^- + C_2H_5OH$$

Equal concentrations of ester and alkali were mixed and the reaction followed. Use the graph below to calculate:

- the initial rate of reaction
- the rate when the concentration of the ester has dropped to 0.032 mol dm^{-3}

Hence deduce the order of the reaction.

Answer

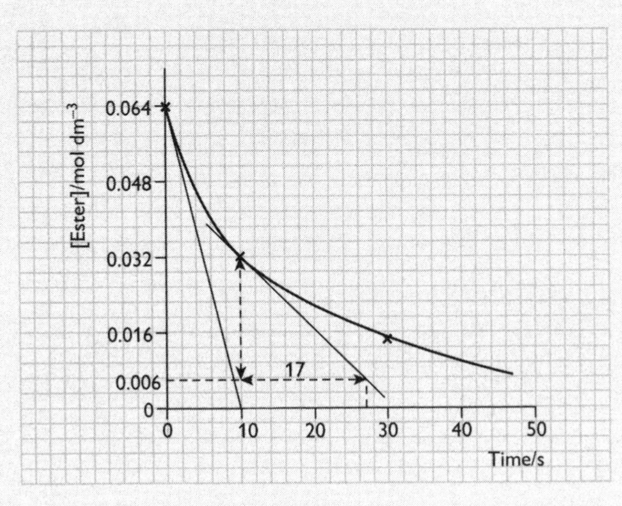

- The gradient of the graph at time zero = $\frac{0.064}{10}$ = 0.0064 mol dm^{-3} s^{-1}. This is the initial rate of reaction.
- The gradient at an ester concentration of 0.032 mol dm^{-3} = $\frac{0.026}{17}$ = 0.0015 mol dm^{-3} s^{-1}
- When the concentration halved, the rate went down by a factor of approximately four (2^2). Therefore, the reaction is second order.

Note: you cannot tell whether the reaction is first order in both reactants or second order with respect to either one. This method tells you the *total* order, unless one reactant is in large excess, in which case the order found will equal the order with respect to the non-excess reagent.

This method can also be used if the concentration (or amount) of product is measured and plotted against time. The only difference is that the graph starts at zero concentration and rises at a decreasing rate. As before, you have to measure the gradient at two different points — usually at zero time and halfway through the reaction.

(2) Use the graph to calculate half-lives

If you are asked to do this, you can expect that the half-lives will be constant within experimental error.

You measure the *time* taken for:

- the concentration to halve from the original value (e.g. from 1.2 to 0.6 units)
- the concentration to halve again (from 0.6 to 0.3)
- the concentration to halve a third time (from 0.3 to 0.15)

These three half-lives should be almost the same. If so, the actual half-life is taken as the average of the three and the reaction is first order.

Worked example

Dinitrogen pentoxide decomposes according to the equation

$$2N_2O_5(g) \longrightarrow 4NO_2(g) + O_2(g)$$

Use the graph below to calculate the half-life of the reaction and determine the order of reaction.

What does this tell you about the mechanism of the reaction?

Answer

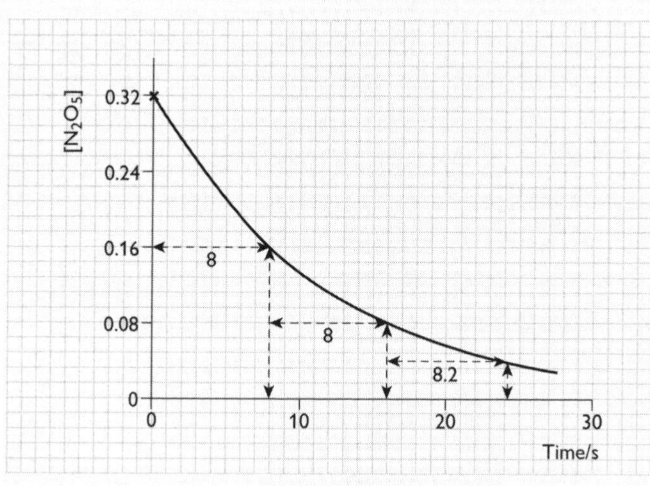

The half-life from $[N_2O_5]$ of 0.32 to $[N_2O_5]$ of 0.16 units = 8.0 s
The half-life from $[N_2O_5]$ of 0.16 to $[N_2O_5]$ of 0.08 units = 8.0 s
The half-life from $[N_2O_5]$ of 0.08 to $[N_2O_5]$ of 0.04 units = 8.2 s

These half-lives are constant within experimental error, so the reaction is first order.

The half life is $\frac{(8.0 + 8.0 + 8.2)}{3} = 8.1\text{ s}$

As the reaction is first order, only 1 molecule of dinitrogen pentoxide is involved in, or before, the rate-determining step.

(3) Deduce the order from the shape of the graph

If the graph of the concentration of a reactant against time is a straight line, the reaction is zero order with respect to that reagent.

A straight line has a constant gradient and therefore the rate is also constant. Since the rate does not alter as the concentration of the reactant decreases, the rate is *independent* of the concentration of that reactant and this is why it is zero order.

Worked example

The acid-catalysed reaction between propanone and iodine is carried out with a large excess of propanone and acid. In one such experiment, the concentration of iodine was found at different times. The results are plotted on the graph below.

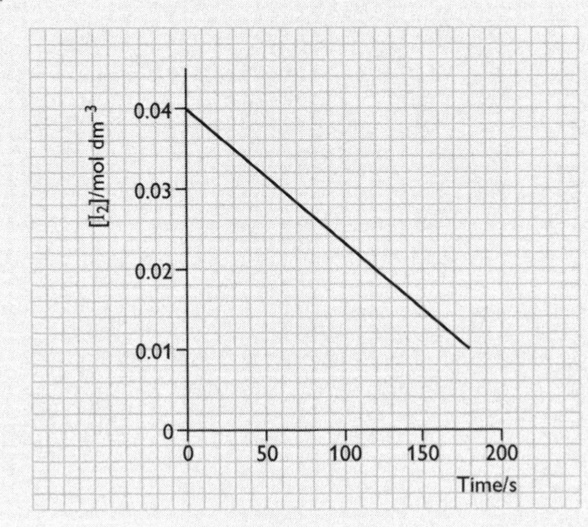

Deduce the order of reaction with respect to iodine and use the result to say where iodine molecules occur in the following mechanism:

$$CH_3COCH_3 + I_2 \longrightarrow CH_2ICOCH_3 + HI$$

Answer

As the graph is a straight line, its gradient is constant. Therefore, the rate of reaction is constant and the reaction is zero order with respect to iodine.

This means that iodine molecules enter the mechanism *after* the rate-determining step.

Gravimetric analysis calculations

This type of calculation involves the reaction of a known mass of starting material to form a precipitate, which is then weighed.

The question will either require you to find out the molar mass and hence the formula of the starting material or, if its identity is given in the question, to find its percentage purity.

The way to do these calculations is to:

- convert the mass of precipitate into moles of precipitate
- then use the stoichiometry of the reaction to work out the moles of starting material

Identifying a substance

Worked example

An organic compound X was analysed in a mass spectrometer. The spectrum showed a molecular ion at *m/e* value 310. It is known that the compound contains carbon, hydrogen, oxygen and iodine only.

A sample of mass 3.84 g of substance X was taken and heated under reflux with sodium hydroxide solution. It was then cooled and excess nitric acid was added, followed by excess silver nitrate solution.

The precipitate of silver iodide was filtered, washed, dried and weighed. The precipitate had a mass of 5.82 g.

(In this and other questions, use the periodic table on page 84 to obtain relative atomic masses.)

(a) Calculate the number of iodine atoms in a molecule of X.

(b) X gave a precipitate with 2,4-dinitrophenylhydrazine but did not react with Fehling's solution. Identify substance X.

Answer

(a) The molar mass of AgI is $235\,g\,mol^{-1}$.

Amount of AgI in the precipitate $= \frac{5.82\,g}{235\,g\,mol^{-1}} = 0.0248\,mol$

Amount of iodine atoms in the sample of X = 0.0248 mol

Amount of X $= \frac{3.84\,g}{310\,g\,mol^{-1}} = 0.0124\,mol$

0.0124 mol X produces 0.0248 mol iodine atoms.

Ratio of moles of iodine atoms to moles of X $= \frac{0.0248}{0.0124} = 2.00$

Therefore, there are two iodine atoms in one molecule of X.

(b) X forms a precipitate with 2,4-dinitrophenylhydrazine, so it is a carbonyl compound. There is no reaction with Fehling's solution, so it is a ketone and not an aldehyde.

The mass of one C=O group and two I atoms is 282. X has a molar mass of $310\,g\,mol^{-1}$. The difference between the molar masses is 28, which is equivalent to two carbon atoms and four hydrogen atoms. Therefore, X is CHI_2COCH_3.

Note: halogeno-compounds are hydrolysed by sodium hydroxide solution to give halide ions, which then form a precipitate with silver nitrate in acidic solution.

Percentage purity calculations

These usually involve simple ionic precipitation reactions, such as the precipitation of sulphate ions by barium ions.

$$Ba^{2+}(aq) + SO_4^{2-}(aq) \longrightarrow BaSO_4(s)$$

General method

- Use the given mass of the precipitate to calculate the number of moles of the precipitate.
- Then use the chemical equation to calculate the number of moles of pure starting material and hence its mass.
- Finally, this mass and the mass of impure substance are used to calculate the % purity.

Alternatively, if the % purity is given:

- Calculate the number of moles of pure starting material using the % purity.
- Use the stoichiometry of the precipitation reaction to calculate the moles of product precipitated.
- Convert this to mass and see if it agrees with the data.

Sometimes the mole ratio is not 1:1, as in the example below.

Worked example

A fertiliser was labelled as containing 32% potassium phosphate, K_3PO_4. A sample of fertiliser weighing 3.85 g was dissolved in water and excess calcium chloride in dilute nitric acid was added. The precipitate of calcium phosphate, $Ca_3(PO_4)_2$, was filtered, washed and dried. It was found to have a mass of 0.901 g. Show that this is consistent with the quoted percentage of potassium phosphate. The equation is:

$$2PO_4^{3-}(aq) + 3Ca^{2+}(aq) \longrightarrow Ca_3(PO_4)_2(s)$$

Answer

Mass of potassium phosphate in the sample $= 3.85 \times \frac{32}{100} = 1.232\,g$

Molar mass of $K_3PO_4 = 212\,g\,mol^{-1}$

Amount of potassium phosphate in sample $= \frac{1.232\,g}{212\,g\,mol^{-1}} = 0.00581\,mol$

1 mol of K_3PO_4 gives 1 mol of PO_4^{3-}, which forms 0.5 mol of $Ca_3(PO_4)_2$.

Amount of $Ca_3(PO_4)_2 = 0.5 \times 0.00581 = 0.002906\,mol$

Mass of $Ca_3(PO_4)_2 = 0.002906\,mol \times 310\,g\,mol^{-1} = 0.901\,g$

This agrees with the data given, so the percentage is correct.

Tip Alternatively, calculate the number of moles of calcium phosphate, then the number of moles and hence the mass of pure potassium phosphate, then the percentage.

Calculations to determine formulae

One example of this is the determination of the number of molecules of water of crystallisation by reacting a known mass of a hydrated salt with an excess of a substance in solution, to form a precipitate.

Worked example

A sample of hydrated sodium carbonate, $Na_2CO_3.xH_2O$, weighing 2.86 g, was dissolved in water, and excess barium chloride solution added. The precipitate of barium carbonate produced had a mass of 1.97 g. Calculate the value of *x* and write the formula of hydrated sodium carbonate.

Answer

$$\text{Amount of barium carbonate} = \frac{1.97\,\text{g}}{197\,\text{g mol}^{-1}} = 0.0100\,\text{mol}$$

The precipitation reaction is

$$Ba^{2+}(aq) + CO_3^{2-}(aq) \longrightarrow BaCO_3(s)$$

The ratio of CO_3^{2-} to Ba^{2+} is 1:1.

Amount of sodium carbonate = 0.0100 mol

$$\text{Molar mass of hydrated sodium carbonate} = \frac{2.86\,\text{g}}{0.0100\,\text{mol}} = 286\,\text{g mol}^{-1}$$

Na_2CO_3 contributes 106 to this molar mass. The difference is 180, which is 10 × 18 (the molar mass of water). Therefore, *x* is 10. There are 10 molecules of water of crystallisation in hydrated sodium carbonate, which has the formula $Na_2CO_3.10H_2O$

Unusual gas volume calculations

The central point in these calculations is the conversion of a volume of gas to moles of that gas, or vice versa. You will always be told the volume occupied by 1 mol of gas (also called the molar volume) under the conditions of the experiment. The value given is usually either 24.0 $dm^3\,mol^{-1}$ or 24 000 $cm^3\,mol^{-1}$. For example:

$$321\,\text{cm}^3 \text{ of gas contains } \frac{321\,\text{cm}^3}{24\,000\,\text{cm}^3\,\text{mol}^{-1}} = 0.0134\,\text{mol}$$

$$\left(\text{moles} = \frac{\text{volume}}{\text{molar volume}}\right)$$

Similarly, 0.123 mol of a gas will occupy 0.123 mol × 24.0 $dm^3\,mol^{-1}$ = 2.95 dm^3.

(volume = moles × molar volume)

Note: the *amount* of a substance is measured as the number of *moles*.

Mineral composition from gas volume

In the example below, the volume of gas produced on decomposition of a mineral is measured, enabling you to check its composition.

Worked example

Dolomite is a mixture of calcium carbonate and magnesium carbonate. Both compounds decompose on heating, forming a metal oxide and carbon dioxide.

$MCO_3(s) \longrightarrow MO(s) + CO_2(g)$

When 2.80 g of dolomite was heated, 0.749 dm^3 of carbon dioxide gas was produced. Show that this volume is consistent with dolomite being composed of 40% calcium carbonate and 60% magnesium carbonate. 1 mol of gas occupies 24.0 dm^3 under the conditions of the experiment.

Answer

Both the calcium carbonate and the magnesium carbonate produce carbon dioxide when heated.

Mass of $CaCO_3$ in 2.80 g of dolomite $= \frac{2.80 \times 40}{100} = 1.12\,g\,CaCO_3$

Amount of $CaCO_3 = \frac{1.12\,g}{100\,g\,mol^{-1}} = 0.0112\,mol\,CaCO_3$

Amount of CO_2 produced from $CaCO_3 = 0.0112\,mol$

Volume of CO_2 from $CaCO_3 = 0.0112\,mol \times 24.0\,dm^3\,mol^{-1} = 0.269\,dm^3$

Mass of $MgCO_3 = \frac{2.80 \times 60}{100} = 1.68\,g$

Amount of $MgCO_3 = \frac{1.68\,g}{84\,g\,mol^{-1}} = 0.0200\,mol$

Amount of CO_2 produced from $MgCO_3 = 0.0200\,mol$

Volume of CO_2 from $MgCO_3 = 0.0200\,mol \times 24.0\,dm^3\,mol^{-1} = 0.480\,dm^3$

Total volume of carbon dioxide $= 0.269 + 0.480 = 0.749\,dm^3$

This is consistent with the data.

Gas volume questions involving titration calculations

For titration calculations, you must know that:

- the amount (moles) of solute = concentration (mol dm^{-3}) × volume (dm^3)
- the volume in dm^3 equals the volume in cm^3 divided by 1000
- the ratio of moles of one substance to another is determined by the stoichiometry of the reaction. For example, if the equation is $2A + 3B \longrightarrow C + 4D$:

  Moles of A $= \frac{\text{stoichiometric No. of A in equation} \times \text{moles of B}}{\text{stoichiometric No. of B in equation}} = \frac{2}{3} \times$ moles of B

  Moles of B $= \frac{3}{1} \times$ moles of C

  Moles of D $= \frac{4}{2} \times$ moles of A

Be careful when only some of the solution is taken and titrated. You must then use a scale-up factor to calculate the *total* number of moles.

All the above points are needed in the following question.

Worked example

The solubility of a gas is the volume of gas that will dissolve in 1 dm^3 of solvent.

Excess solid potassium hydroxide and excess solid manganese(IV) oxide were added to 500 cm^3 of water that had been saturated with oxygen. The following reaction took place:

$$3O_2(aq) + 4MnO_2(s) + 4KOH(s) \longrightarrow 4KMnO_4(aq) + 2H_2O(l)$$

The mixture was allowed to settle and 250 cm^3 of the clear solution containing potassium manganate(VII) was removed, acidified and titrated with 0.0200 mol dm^{-3} of iron(II) sulphate solution. Acidified manganate(VII) and iron(II) react according to the equation:

$$8H^+(aq) + 5Fe^{2+}(aq) + MnO_4^-(aq) \longrightarrow 5Fe^{3+}(aq) + Mn^{2+}(aq) + 4H_2O(l)$$

The titre was 21.8 cm^3 of the iron(II) sulphate solution. Calculate the solubility of oxygen gas in water, given that 1 mol of gas occupies 24.0 dm^3 under the experimental conditions.

Answer

Amount of Fe^{2+} ions = 0.0200 mol dm^{-3} × 0.0218 dm^3 = 0.000436 mol

Amount of MnO_4^- ions in 250 cm^3 = $\frac{1}{5}$ × 0.000436 = 0.0000872 mol

Amount of MnO_4^- ions in 500 cm^3 = 2 × 0.0000872 = 0.0001744 mol

Amount of dissolved oxygen in 500 cm^3 = $\frac{3}{4}$ × 0.0001744 = 0.000131 mol

Amount of oxygen that would dissolve in 1 dm^3 of water = 2 × 0.000131
= 0.000262 mol

Volume of oxygen = 0.000262 mol × 24.0 dm^3 mol^{-1} = 0.00629 dm^3

Solubility of oxygen in water = 0.00629 dm^3 of oxygen per dm^3 water

Unusual titrations

There are three types of unusual titration calculation that you may encounter.

(1) Back titrations

In a back titration, excess of substance A is added to B. All substance B reacts. The excess A is diluted to a given volume and portions of this are then titrated using a third substance, C. The steps in the calculation are:

Step 1: Calculate the moles of C in the titre.
Step 2: Calculate the moles of A in excess in one portion.
Step 3: Calculate the moles of A in excess in the total volume of diluted solution.
Step 4: Calculate the moles of A originally taken.
Step 5: By subtraction, calculate the moles of A that reacted with B.
Step 6: Calculate the moles of B and hence its mass, concentration or purity.

You must use the stoichiometry of the A + C reaction in Step 2 and that of the A + B reaction in Step 6. If you are not given one of the equations, you *must* write it in your answer.

Worked example

Aspirin is 2-ethanoyloxybenzoic acid. It has the following formula:

It is too insoluble to be titrated directly.

Five aspirin tablets were crushed and placed in a flask. 50.0 cm^3 of 1.00 mol dm^{-3} sodium hydroxide solution was added and the solution heated until all the aspirin had reacted. The equation for this reaction is

$$CH_3COOC_6H_4COOH + 2NaOH \longrightarrow CH_3COONa + HOC_6H_4COONa + H_2O$$

The solution was cooled and made up to 250 cm^3 with distilled water. 25.0 cm^3 portions of this diluted solution, containing excess sodium hydroxide, were titrated against 0.0750 mol dm^{-3} sulphuric acid. The mean titre was 22.0 cm^3. Calculate the mass, in milligrams, of aspirin in one tablet.

Answer

Step 1: Amount of sulphuric acid in the titre = 0.0750 mol dm^{-3} × 0.0220 dm^3
= 0.00165 mol

Step 2: Equation:

$$H_2SO_4 + 2NaOH \longrightarrow Na_2SO_4 + 2H_2O$$

Amount of excess NaOH in 25 cm^3 = $\frac{2}{1}$ × 0.00165 = 0.00330 mol

Step 3: Total amount of excess NaOH = 10 × 0.00330 = 0.0330 mol

Step 4: Amount of NaOH originally taken = 0.050 dm^3 × 1.00 mol dm^{-3}
= 0.0500 mol

Step 5: Amount of NaOH reacted with aspirin = 0.0500 – 0.0330
= 0.0170 mol

Step 6: Amount of aspirin in five tablets = $\frac{1}{2} \times 0.0170 = 0.00850$ mol

Amount of aspirin in one tablet = $\frac{1}{5} \times 0.00850 = 0.00170$ mol

Molar mass of aspirin = $(9 \times 12) + (8 \times 1) + (4 \times 16) = 180\,g\,mol^{-1}$

Mass of aspirin in one tablet = $0.00170\,mol \times 180\,g\,mol^{-1}$
= 0.306 g = 306 mg

(2) Unusual redox reactions

This is probably the easiest type, as the equation will be given to you and the remainder of the calculation is straightforward.

Worked example

Sodium dithionite, $Na_2S_2O_4$, can be used to estimate the concentration of chromate(VI) ions because, when made alkaline, it reacts rapidly and quantitatively, even in dilute solution:

$$3S_2O_4^{2-} + 2CrO_4^{2-} + 2H_2O + 2OH^- \longrightarrow 6SO_3^{2-} + 2Cr(OH)_3$$

In a titration, 10.0 dm^3 of waste water from a chrome plating plant required 27.6 cm^3 of a 0.0258 $mol\,dm^{-3}$ sodium dithionite solution. Calculate the concentration, in $mol\,dm^{-3}$, of chromate(VI) ions in the waste water and then the mass of chromium in parts per million (ppm).

Answer

Amount of sodium dithionite = $0.0276\,dm^3 \times 0.0258\,mol\,dm^{-3} = 0.0007121$ mol

Amount of CrO_4^{2-} ions = $\frac{2}{3} \times 0.0007121 = 0.0004747$ mol

Concentration of chromate(VI) ions in the waste water = $\frac{0.0004747\,mol}{10.0\,dm^3}$
= $0.0000475\,mol\,dm^{-3}$

Mass of Cr = $0.0000475\,mol\,dm^{-3} \times 52\,g\,mol^{-1} = 0.00247\,g\,dm^{-3}$ in 1000 g water

Therefore, mass of Cr in 1 million grams of water = 0.00247×1000
= 2.47 g = 2.47 ppm

Note: this would exceed the EU maximum discharge limit.

(3) Deriving equations from titration data

It is possible to work out reactant ratios and hence derive the formula of a product and the overall chemical equation. This would probably be asked about a reaction that is new to you, so that you do not know the answer but have to work it out from the data.

Worked example

Manganate(VII) ions oxidise mercury metal to mercury cations in acid solution and are themselves reduced to Mn^{2+} ions.

In a titration, 0.672 g of mercury required 28.0 cm³ of 0.0480 mol dm⁻³ potassium manganate(VII) solution for complete reaction. Calculate the change in oxidation number of the mercury and hence derive the equation.

Answer

Amount of mercury = $\frac{0.672\,\text{g}}{201\,\text{g mol}^{-1}}$ = 0.00334 mol

Amount of potassium manganate(VII) = $0.0280\ \text{dm}^3 \times 0.0480\ \text{mol dm}^{-3}$
= 0.00134 mol

Hg and MnO_4^{2-} react in the mole ratio of $\frac{0.00334}{0.00134}$ = 2.5:1 or 5:2

The oxidation number of each Mn in MnO_4^- changes from +7 to +2 (down by 5).

The total change is down by 10. Therefore, the oxidation number of five Hg atoms must go up by a total of 10 (up 2 each).

The oxidation state of mercury changes from 0 to +2. Hg^{2+} ions are formed from Hg atoms.

The equation is:

$$5Hg + 2MnO_4^- + 16H^+ \longrightarrow 5Hg^{2+} + 2Mn^{2+} + 8H_2O$$

Tip If you have practised all these questions, you will not only be able to tackle any calculation in Question 1 of the Unit 6B test but will also have covered a number of topics, such as kinetics.

Section B

The questions in Section B of the unit test embrace the whole specification, particularly the topics covered at A2. Each synoptic question may include several topics and will often be about substances that are new to you. The skill of drawing together knowledge and understanding from different topics must be practised, as must using the data provided, together with your knowledge of similar substances, to deduce the answer. Understanding, rather than rote learning, is the key to success in Unit 6B.

In the following sections, several topics that are particularly suitable for synoptic questions are reviewed in order to improve your understanding.

Forces between particles

This topic could appear in almost any synoptic question.

Chemical bonding

The strongest forces are those associated with chemical bonding.

Ionic bonds

The strength of an ionic bond depends mainly on:

- the charges on the ions — the larger the charges, the stronger the force
- the sum of the ionic radii — the larger the sum, the weaker the force

Strong ion–ion forces cause a substance to have a high melting temperature and a large exothermic lattice energy.

Covalent bonds

- Covalent bond strength is similar to ionic bond strength.
- Generally, covalent bonds between small atoms are stronger than those between larger atoms.
- Short bonds are stronger than long bonds.
- A double bond is stronger than a single bond.
- Polar bonds, such as C–F, are stronger than non-polar bonds, such as C–C.
- Strength is measured by bond enthalpy — the bigger the bond enthalpy, the stronger the covalent bond.
- Bond *breaking* requires forces of attraction to be overcome and so it is always *endothermic*. Bond *making* is always *exothermic*.
- When a covalent substance is melted or boiled, covalent bonds are *not* broken and so the melting and boiling temperatures of a covalent substance are *not* determined by the strength of the *covalent* bonds within the molecule. The melting and boiling temperatures depend upon the strength of the *intermolecular* forces, which have to be overcome when the substance melts or boils.
- A strong covalent bond results in a high activation energy. Hence, reactions involving breaking that bond are slow. Therefore, chloroalkanes (C–Cl, bond enthalpy +338 kJ mol^{-1}) are hydrolysed by hydroxide ions more slowly than bromoalkanes (C–Br, bond enthalpy +276 kJ mol^{-1}).

Bond	Sum of covalent radii/nm	Bond enthalpy/kJ mol^{-1}
C–H	0.11	+412
C–C	0.15	+348
C=C	0.13	+612
C=O	0.12	+743
C–F	0.15	+484
C–Cl	0.18	+338
C–Br	0.19	+276

Forces between covalent molecules

Forces between covalent molecules are called intermolecular forces. They are much weaker than chemical bonds.

Hydrogen bonds

Hydrogen bonds are the strongest intermolecular forces. They result from the attraction between a δ+ hydrogen atom in one molecule and a δ– nitrogen, oxygen or fluorine atom in another molecule. The two atoms in a hydrogen bond are polar and very small.

The bond enthalpy of an O–H⋯O hydrogen bond is +20 kJ mol^{-1}, which is considerably less than the +463 kJ mol^{-1} bond enthalpy of the covalent O–H bond.

Permanent dipole–dipole forces

Permanent dipole–dipole forces are much weaker than hydrogen bonds. In liquids and gases, values are typically less than 0.5 kJ mol^{-1}. They only occur between polar molecules in which the δ+ end of one molecule is attracted to the δ– end of another molecule.

Instantaneous induced dipole–induced dipole forces

Instantaneous induced dipole–induced dipole forces are also called dispersion forces. In most compounds, they are stronger than permanent dipole–dipole forces but weaker than hydrogen bonds. They arise because the electron cloud in a molecule oscillates and sets up an in-phase oscillation with the electrons in neighbouring molecules.

The size of the force depends mostly on:

- the number of electrons in each molecule. The more electrons there are in each molecule, the stronger the force between the molecules. Multi-electron molecules, such as I_2 with 106 electrons, have large instantaneous induced dipole–induced dipole forces and so are solids at room temperature. Methane, CH_4, with only 10 electrons, is a gas with a boiling temperature of −162°C.
- the number of points of contact between the two molecules. There are more points of contact between straight-chain molecules than between highly branched molecules.

Solubility

This topic can be covered in a number of contexts and so is particularly suitable for synoptic questions. It incorporates intermolecular forces, bonding, acids and bases and energetics.

The key to solubility is that the strength of the solvent–solute forces must be similar to the average strength of the solvent–solvent and the solute–solute forces.

Tip Avoid using phrases such as 'like dissolves like' (this is too vague) and 'polar solvents dissolve polar molecules' (this is not always true).

The first question that you must ask yourself is, *what is the type of bonding in the solute?*

Solubility of ionic solutes

Many ionic substances dissolve in water. This is because of the strong forces between:

- the cation (positive) and the δ– oxygen in the water
- the anion (negative) and the δ+ hydrogen in the water

These ion–dipole forces are very strong and so may be similar to the strong ion–ion forces in the solid.

The guide here is that the less endothermic (or more exothermic) the enthalpy of solution, the more soluble is the ionic solid.

The enthalpy of solution can be calculated using a Hess's law cycle. For example, for an ionic solid such as calcium fluoride, CaF_2:

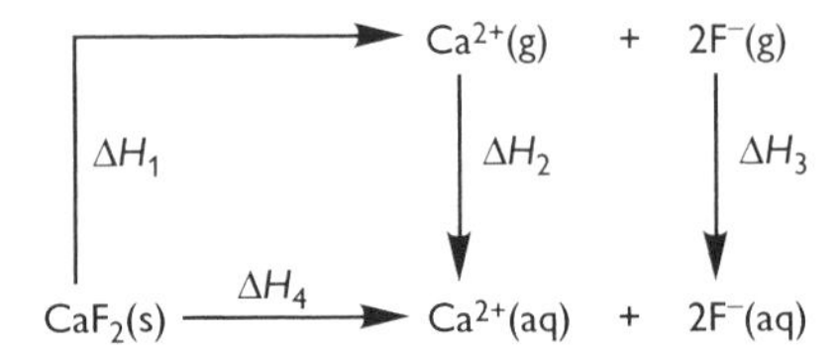

$$\Delta H_4 = \Delta H_1 + \Delta H_2 + \Delta H_3$$

where:

ΔH_1 = –lattice energy of $CaF_2(s)$
ΔH_2 = enthalpy of hydration of $Ca^{2+}(g)$
ΔH_3 = 2 × enthalpy of hydration of $F^-(g)$
ΔH_4 = enthalpy of solution of solid CaF_2 = ΔH_{soln}
ΔH_{soln} = –lattice energy of $CaF_2(s)$ + hydration enthalpy of $Ca^{2+}(g)$ + 2 × hydration enthalpy of $F^-(g)$

Solubility of covalent substances in water

Water readily dissolves covalent substances only if the covalent substance can either form hydrogen bonds with water molecules or react with the water to form ions.

Solubility and hydrogen bonds

- Organic compounds with –OH, –C=O, –COOH, $–NH_2$ or –NH groups are soluble, provided that the rest of the molecule is not too large.
- Short-chain alcohols dissolve because the δ– oxygen atoms in the alcohols form hydrogen bonds with the δ+ hydrogen atoms in the water, and the δ+ hydrogen atoms in the alcohols form hydrogen bonds with the δ– oxygen atoms in the water.
- Urea, NH_2CONH_2, is used as a fertiliser. It is very soluble in water because the oxygen and nitrogen atoms in urea form hydrogen bonds with the δ+ hydrogen atoms in water molecules, and the δ+ hydrogen atoms in urea form hydrogen bonds with the δ– oxygen atoms in the water.

Tip Remember, hydrogen bonds can only form between δ+ hydrogen atoms and δ– nitrogen, oxygen or fluorine atoms. Other atoms (e.g. chlorine) are too large or not sufficiently electronegative (e.g. carbon).

Solubility and reaction with water

- Acids, such as hydrogen chloride, are covalent but dissolve in water. This is because they *react* with the water to form ions.

  $HCl(g) + H_2O(l) \longrightarrow H_3O^+(aq) + Cl^-(aq)$
- Ammonia is covalent and very soluble, because it reacts partially with water to form ions.

  $NH_3(g) + H_2O(l) \rightleftharpoons NH_4^+(aq) + OH^-(aq)$

  Also, the covalent ammonia molecules form hydrogen bonds with the water.

Tip The statement that 'polar molecules dissolve in water' is not correct unless they form strong hydrogen bonds with water. The very polar chloroethane and ethoxyethane are insoluble.

Solubility of covalent substances in non-aqueous solvents

- The forces involved are intermolecular van der Waals forces. For a substance A to dissolve in substance B, the A–B intermolecular forces must be similar to the A–A and the B–B intermolecular forces.
- The most important force to be considered is the instantaneous induced dipole–induced dipole force. The size of the force depends mainly on the number of electrons in the molecules.
- Solubility is likely to occur if the solvent and solute molecules are similar in type. For example, benzene (C_6H_6) and methylbenzene ($C_6H_5CH_3$) are miscible in all proportions.

'Dissolving' in acids or bases

You will often come across phrases such as 'magnesium dissolves in hydrochloric acid' or 'amphoteric hydroxides dissolve in excess alkali'. It is more correct to state that the solid substance reacts to form a solution.

Amphoteric hydroxides

The amphoteric hydroxides you need to know are the hydrated hydroxides of aluminium, chromium(III), zinc and lead(II). These are deprotonated by excess strong alkali to form soluble anions.

The equation for aluminium and chromium, which are in the +3 state, is:

$$[M(H_2O)_3(OH)_3](s) + 3OH^-(aq) \longrightarrow [M(OH)_6]^{3-}(aq) + 3H_2O(l)$$

The equation for zinc and lead(II), which are in the +2 state, is:

$$[M(H_2O)_2(OH)_2](s) + 2OH^-(aq) \longrightarrow [M(OH)_4]^{2-}(aq) + 2H_2O(l)$$

A solution is formed because the insoluble covalent substance reacts to form an ion.

d-block metals which form ammines

The hydroxides of cobalt, nickel, copper and zinc 'dissolve' in excess ammonia solution. The mechanism involves ligand exchange, in which hydroxide ions and water molecules are replaced by ammonia molecules. The product is ionic and is therefore soluble. For example:

$$[Cu(H_2O)_4(OH)_2](s) + 4NH_3(aq) \longrightarrow 2OH^-(aq) + 2H_2O(l) + [Cu(NH_3)_4(H_2O)_2]^{2+}(aq)$$

Chromium(III) hydroxide slowly forms an ammine with concentrated ammonia, but the reaction needs a long time to go to completion.

Aromatic acids and bases

Benzoic acid is almost insoluble in cold water. However, if a solution of a strong alkali (e.g. sodium hydroxide) is added to benzoic acid, it does form a solution. This is because it reacts to form an ionic salt, which is more soluble than the covalent molecule, even though the molecule can form hydrogen bonds with water.

$$C_6H_5COOH(s) + Na^+OH^-(aq) \longrightarrow C_6H_5COO^-Na^+(aq) + H_2O(l)$$

Similarly, the weak base phenylamine forms a solution when a strong acid is added. This is also because of the formation of an ionic salt:

$$C_6H_5NH_2(l) + H^+Cl^-(aq) \longrightarrow C_6H_5NH_3^+Cl^-(aq)$$

Energetics

You must be able to draw a Hess's law cycle and a Born–Haber cycle, and be able to calculate the enthalpy of reaction.

Hess's law cycles

Hess's law states that the enthalpy change from reactants to products in a one-step reaction is the same as the sum of the enthalpy changes for all the reactions in a multi-step sequence. For example:

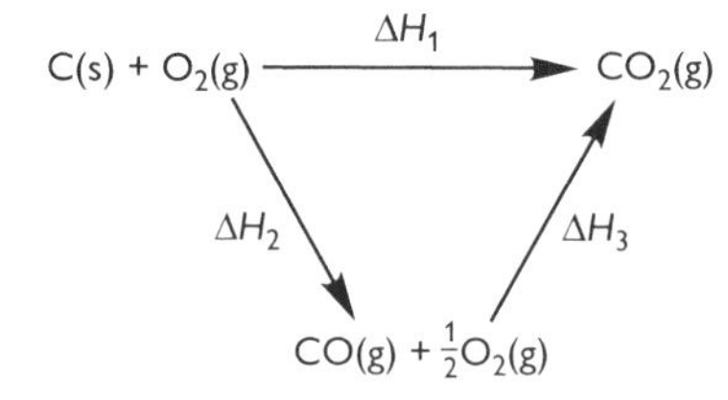

where $\Delta H_1 = \Delta H_2 + \Delta H_3$.

Born–Haber cycles

A Born–Haber cycle relates the enthalpy of formation of an ionic solid to the enthalpies of atomisation, ionisation energies, electron affinities and lattice energy. The Born–Haber cycle for magnesium fluoride is:

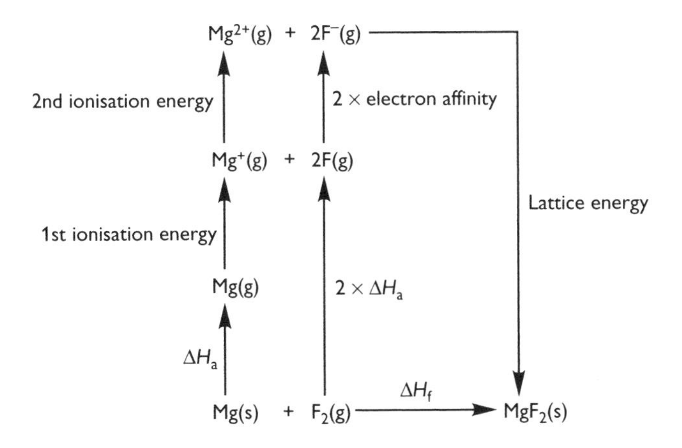

where ΔH_f is the enthalpy of formation and ΔH_a is the enthalpy of atomisation.

By Hess's law, ΔH_f = the sum of the other terms in the cycle.

Remember:

- ΔH_a is the enthalpy change that occurs when 1 mol of gaseous atoms is formed from the element in its standard state. Therefore, the changes:
  $F_2(g) \longrightarrow 2F(g)$
  $I_2(s) \longrightarrow 2I(g)$
  are both $2 \times \Delta H_a$
- The lattice energy is the exothermic energy change for the formation of 1 mol of ionic solid from its gaseous ions.

Enthalpy of reaction calculations

Bond enthalpy data

You have to work out which bonds have to be broken (an endothermic process) and which made (an exothermic process). The sum of the positive bond-breaking and the negative bond-making enthalpies is the enthalpy of reaction.

Worked example

The enthalpy of the reaction $H_2C{=}CH_2 + H_2O \longrightarrow H_3C{-}CH_2OH$ can be calculated using bond enthalpy values.

Bond	Bond enthalpy/kJ mol^{-1}
C=C	+612
C–C	+348
H–O	+463
C–O	+360
C–H	+412

Answer

Bonds broken	Enthalpy change/ kJ mol^{-1}	Bonds made	Enthalpy change/ kJ mol^{-1}
1 C=C	+612	1 C–C	–348
1 H–O	+463	1 C–O	–360
		1 C–H	–412
Total	+1075	Total	–1120

The enthalpy of the reaction, ΔH_r, is given by:

$\Delta H_r = +1075 + (-1120) = -45\,\text{kJ mol}^{-1}$

Enthalpy of formation data

Calculating the enthalpy of reaction from enthalpy of formation data should be done using a Hess's law cycle, which will be of the form:

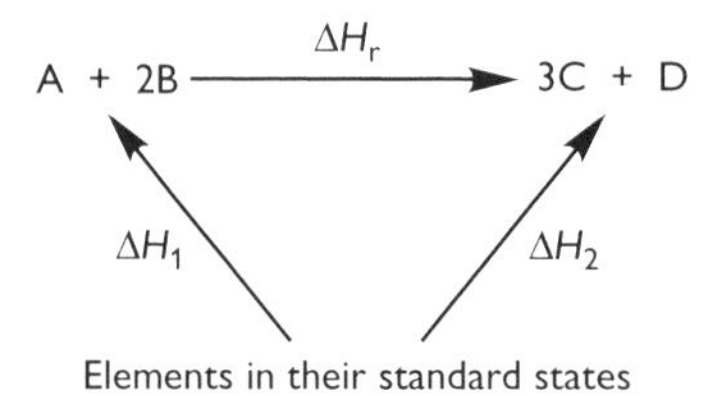

where

$\Delta H_1 = \Delta H_f$ of A + 2 × ΔH_f of B

$\Delta H_2 = 3 \times \Delta H_f$ of C + ΔH_f of D

By Hess's law:

$\Delta H_1 + \Delta H_r = \Delta H_2$

Therefore,

$\Delta H_r = \Delta H_2 - \Delta H_1$

This is often written as:

ΔH_r = the sum of ΔH_f of products – the sum of ΔH_f of reactants

Tip This formula can only be used when enthalpy of *formation* data are supplied. It should *never* be written as ΔH_r= 'products – reactants' or as ΔH_r = '$\Delta H_{products} - \Delta H_{reactants}$'.

Enthalpy of combustion data

Calculating the enthalpy of reaction from enthalpy of combustion (ΔH_c) data is only expected for organic reactions. A Hess's law cycle must be drawn, which will be of the form:

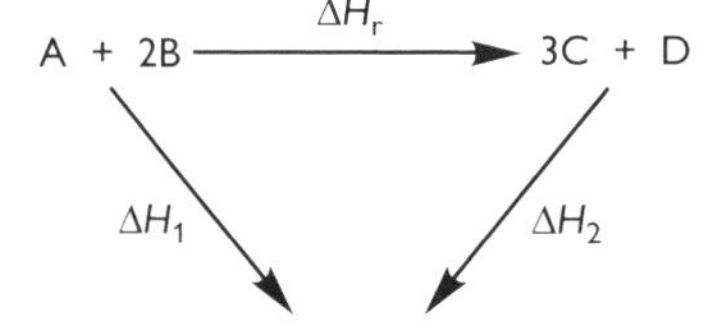

where

$\Delta H_1 = \Delta H_c$ of A + 2 × ΔH_c of B

$\Delta H_2 = 3 \times \Delta H_c$ of C + ΔH_c of D

By Hess's law:

$\Delta H_r + \Delta H_2 = \Delta H_1$

Therefore,

$\Delta H_r = \Delta H_1 - \Delta H_2$

Note that this time:

ΔH_r = the sum of ΔH_c of reactants – the sum of ΔH_c of products

Worked example

Calculate the enthalpy of formation of ethene, given the following enthalpies of combustion:

Substance	ΔH_c/kJ mol^{-1}
Ethene	–1409
Carbon	–394
Hydrogen	–286

Answer

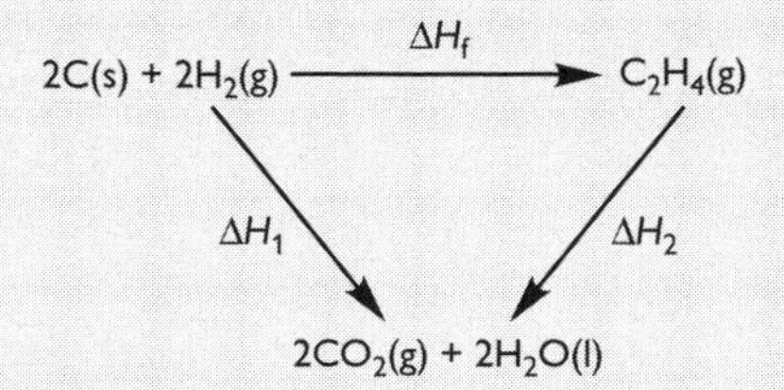

$\Delta H_1 = 2 \times \Delta H_c$ of C + 2 × ΔH_c of H_2 = 2 × (–394) + 2 × (–286) = –1360 kJ

$\Delta H_2 = \Delta H_c$ of ethene = –1409 kJ

$\Delta H_f = \Delta H_1 - \Delta H_2 = -1360 - (-1409) = +49\ \text{kJ mol}^{-1}$

Solubility

You have to be able to discuss solubility of ionic substances in terms of lattice energy and hydration enthalpy (see p. 28).

Equilibrium

Calculation of K_c

The safest way to do the calculation is to draw up a table and work out:

- the moles at the start
- the change in moles on reaching equilibrium — you must use the stoichiometry of the reaction

- the moles at equilibrium
- the concentration at equilibrium

Tip Remember, only *equilibrium* concentrations can be used in the K_c expression.

Worked example

A mixture containing 0.250 mol of nitrogen and 0.400 mol of hydrogen was allowed to reach equilibrium at a temperature of T°C in a vessel of volume 0.500 dm^3. At equilibrium, it was found that 0.0750 mol of ammonia had been produced. Calculate the value of the equilibrium constant, K_c.

Answer

The equation is:

$$N_2(g) + 3H_2(g) \rightleftharpoons 2NH_3(g)$$

So $K_c = \dfrac{[NH_3]^2_{eq}}{[N_2]_{eq}[H_2]^3_{eq}}$

	N_2	$3H_2$	$2NH_3$
Moles at start	0.250	0.400	0
Change	$-\frac{1}{2} \times 0.075 = -0.0375$	$-\frac{3}{2} \times 0.075 = -0.1125$	+0.075
Moles at equilibrium	0.250 – 0.0375 = 0.2125	0.400 – 0.1125 = 0.2875	0.075
Concentration/ mol dm^{-3}	$\frac{0.2125}{0.500} = 0.425$	$\frac{0.2875}{0.500} = 0.575$	$\frac{0.075}{0.500} = 0.150$

$$K_c = \frac{(0.150)^2}{(0.425)(0.575)^3} = 0.278\ \text{mol}^{-2}\,\text{dm}^6$$

Calculation of K_p

To calculate K_p, instead of being told the volume of the container, you will be told the total pressure at equilibrium. The steps are as follows:

- Work out the moles of each substance at equilibrium.
- Calculate the total number of moles and hence the mole fraction of each substance.
- Multiply the mole fractions by the total pressure to obtain the partial pressures.

Worked example

Nitrosyl bromide decomposes according to the following equilibrium:

$$2NOBr(g) \rightleftharpoons 2NO(g) + Br_2(g)$$

In a closed vessel at 25°C, it is 24% dissociated, resulting in a total pressure of 4.00 atm. Calculate the value of K_p.

Tip Assume that there was 1 mol of nitrosyl bromide initially. This is the easiest way to approach decomposition reaction calculations when you are given the percentage reacted or produced.

Answer

$$K_p = \frac{p(NO)^2 \times p(Br_2)}{p(NOBr)^2}$$

	2NOBr	2NO	Br_2
Moles at start	1	0	0
Change	–0.24	+0.24	$+\frac{1}{2} \times 0.24 = 0.12$
Moles at equilibrium	1 – 0.24 = 0.76	0.24	0.12
Mole fraction	$\frac{0.76}{1.12} = 0.679$	$\frac{0.24}{1.12} = 0.214$	$\frac{0.12}{1.12} = 0.107$
Partial pressure/ atm	$0.679 \times 4.00 = 2.72$	$0.214 \times 4.00 = 0.856$	$0.107 \times 4.00 = 0.428$

$$K_p = \frac{(0.856)^2 \times (0.428)}{(2.72)^2} = 0.0424 \text{ atm}$$

Tip To calculate the mole fraction, you need to work out the total moles at equilibrium. In this case, 0.76 + 0.24 + 0.12 = 1.12.

Effect of changes in condition on *K* and the equilibrium position

Temperature

If the temperature is increased in an *exothermic* (ΔH negative) reversible reaction, the value of the equilibrium constant decreases. Therefore, the position of equilibrium shifts to the left and the equilibrium yield decreases. The opposite happens in an endothermic reaction.

An increase in temperature increases the rate at which equilibrium is reached for both exothermic and endothermic reactions.

Pressure

If the pressure on a gaseous equilibrium is increased, the value of *K* does *not* change. However, the equilibrium position shifts towards the side with fewer *gas* molecules. Industrial manufacturing processes involving gases always work at a pressure above atmospheric pressure, even if this lowers the equilibrium yield, because pressure is needed to push the gases through the system.

Catalyst

A catalyst affects neither the value of K nor the position of equilibrium. It causes equilibrium to be reached more rapidly.

Tip Do not use the phrase 'favouring a direction', as its meaning is not clear.

pH of strong acids and bases

- The pH of a strong monobasic acid is given by $pH = -\log_{10}[acid]$.
- The pH of a strong base with one –OH per formula is given by $pH = 14 - pOH$, where $pOH = -\log_{10}[OH^-]$.

Tip To calculate $[H^+]$ given the pH, you need the expression $[H^+] = 10^{-pH}$. Practise doing this on your calculator.

Worked example 1

Calculate the hydrogen ion concentration of a solution of pH 1.23.

Answer

$$[H^+] = 10^{-pH} = 10^{-1.23} = 0.059\,mol\,dm^{-3}$$

Worked example 2

Calculate the pH of a 0.123 mol dm^{-3} solution of the strong base sodium hydroxide, NaOH.

Answer

The base has only 1 mol of OH^- per mole. Therefore:

$[OH^-] = 0.123\,mol\,dm^{-3}$

$pOH = 0.91$

$pH = 14 - 0.91 = 13.09$

Note: if the base had been barium hydroxide, $Ba(OH)_2$, $[OH^-]$ would have been $2 \times 0.123\,mol\,dm^{-3}$.

Tip Always give pH answers to 2 decimal places.

pH and K_a calculations of weak acids

A weak acid, HA, dissociates in water according to the equation:

$$HA \rightleftharpoons H^+ + A^- \quad \text{or} \quad HA + H_2O \rightleftharpoons H_3O^+ + A^-$$

The acid dissociation constant K_a is given by:

$$K_a = \frac{[H^+][A^-]}{[HA]} \quad \text{or} \quad K_a = \frac{[H_3O^+][A^-]}{[HA]}$$

$[H_2O]$ does not appear in the equilibrium expression, as it is the solvent and so its concentration does not alter.

The points to remember in calculations are:

- $[H^+] = [A^-]$
- $[HA]$ = the concentration of the acid given in the question
- $pK_a = -\log_{10}K_a$ and $K_a = 10^{-pK_a}$
- $pH = -\log_{10}[H^+]$ or $[H^+] = 10^{-pH}$

Tip Check your answer to make sure that $[H^+]$ is a number less than 0.01.

Worked example

An ethanoic acid solution of concentration 0.111 mol dm^{-3} has a pH = 2.86.

Calculate the value of the acid dissociation constant, K_a.

Answer

$$K_a = \frac{[H^+][CH_3COO^-]}{[CH_3COOH]}$$

$[H^+] = 10^{-pH} = 10^{-2.86} = 0.00138\ \text{mol dm}^{-3}$

$[CH_3COO^-] = [H^+] = 0.00138\ \text{mol dm}^{-3}$

$[CH_3COOH] = 0.111\ \text{mol dm}^{-3}$

$$K_a = \frac{(0.00138\ \text{mol dm}^{-3})^2}{(0.111\ \text{mol dm}^{-3})} = 1.72 \times 10^{-5}\ \text{mol dm}^{-3}$$

Note: because 0.00138 mol dm^{-3} of acid dissociated, a more accurate way to calculate $[CH_3COOH]$ would be

$[CH_3COOH] = 0.111 - 0.00138 = 0.1096\ \text{mol dm}^{-3}$

Therefore,

$K_a = 1.74 \times 10^{-5}\ \text{mol dm}^{-3}$

pH of buffer solutions

An acid buffer solution consists of a weak acid and its salt. The salt contains the conjugate base of the weak acid. The salt, NaA, of the weak acid is totally ionised:

$NaA \longrightarrow Na^+ + A^-$

The weak acid, HA, is partially ionised, and its ionisation is suppressed by the high value of $[A^-]$ from the salt:

$HA \rightleftharpoons H^+ + A^-$

For all weak acids:

$$K_a = \frac{[H^+][A^-]}{[HA]}$$

However: $[A^-]$ = [salt] and $[HA]$ = [acid]

Therefore: $K_a = \frac{[H^+][\text{salt}]}{[\text{acid}]}$ and $[H^+] = K_a \times \frac{[\text{acid}]}{[\text{salt}]}$

Worked example

Calculate the pH of a buffer solution made by adding 50 cm^3 of 0.300 mol dm^{-3} solution of ethanoic acid, $K_a = 1.74 \times 10^{-5}$ mol dm^{-3}, to 50 cm^3 of a 0.400 mol dm^{-3} solution of sodium ethanoate.

Answer

The total volume of the buffer solution has doubled; therefore, the concentrations of acid and salt have halved.

$[CH_3COOH] = \frac{1}{2} \times 0.300 = 0.150$ mol dm^{-3}

$[CH_3COO^-] = \frac{1}{2} \times 0.400 = 0.200$ mol dm^{-3}

$$[H^+] = K_a \times \frac{[acid]}{[salt]} = 1.74 \times 10^{-5} \times \frac{0.150}{0.200}$$

$$= 1.305 \times 10^{-5} \text{ mol dm}^{-3}$$

$pH = -\log_{10}(1.305 \times 10^{-5}) = 4.88$

Mode of action of a buffer

When a small quantity of acid is added to a buffer, almost all the H^+ ions react with the large excess of A^- ions from the salt, and so the pH hardly alters.

When a small quantity of base is added to a buffer, almost all the OH^- ions react with the large excess of HA molecules (whose ionisation has been suppressed by the A^- ions from the salt), and so the pH hardly alters.

Shapes of molecules

Valance shell electron pair repulsion (VSEPR) theory

- The bond and lone electron pairs around a central atom repel each other to a position of maximum separation.
- The repulsion between a lone pair and a bond pair is greater than that between two bond pairs. Therefore, one or more lone pairs of electrons will reduce the angle between the bond pairs.

Number of pairs of electrons and shapes of molecules

To predict the shape of a molecule or ion, you must first evaluate the number of σ-bond pairs and lone pairs of electrons around the central atom. The shapes then follow. Ignore all π-bond pairs (treat a double bond as one bond pair).

You must practise drawing the following shapes, especially those in three dimensions.

Total number of pairs	Bond pairs	Lone pairs	Shape	Bond angles	Examples
2	2	0	Linear	180°	Cl–Be–Cl, O=C=O, H–C≡N
3	3	0	Trigonal planar 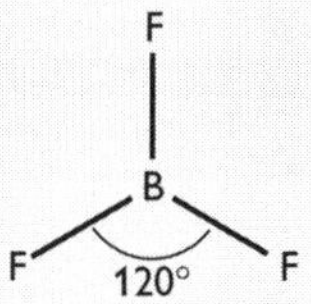	120°	BF_3, SO_3, NO_3^-, CO_3^{2-}
4	4	0	Tetrahedral 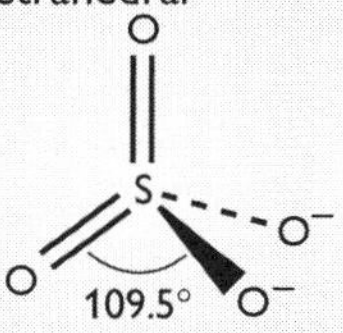	≈109.5°	CH_4, CCl_4, NH_4^+, SO_4^{2-}
4	3	1	Pyramidal 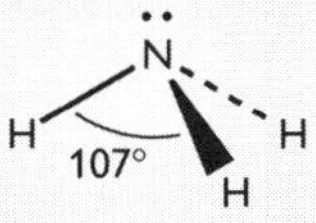 (Electrons are arranged in a tetrahedron)	≈107°	NH_3, PH_3, SO_3^{2-}
4	2	2	V-shape 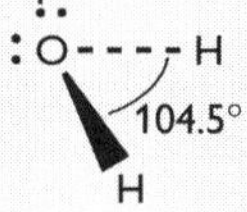	≈104.5°	H_2O, H_2S, NO_2^-
5	5	0	Trigonal bipyramidal 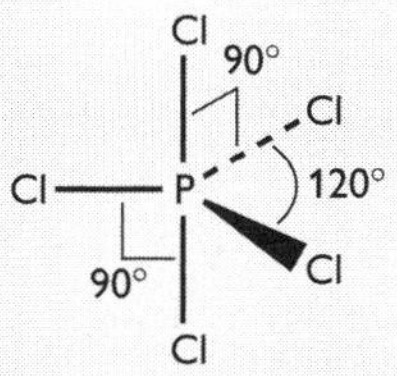	120° in the plane, 90° perpendicular to the plane	PCl_5, PF_5
6	6	0	Octahedral 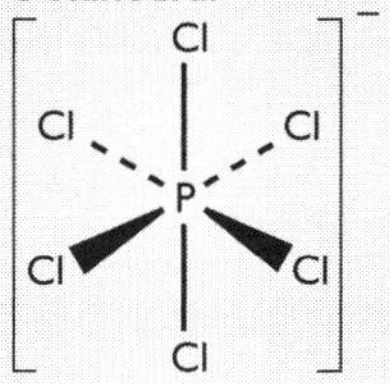	90°	SF_6, $[PCl_6]^-$, all 6-coordinate complexes of metal ions (e.g. $[Al(H_2O)_6]^{3+}$and $[Cr(NH_3)_6]^{3+}$)

Questions & Answers

Most of the following questions are drawn from three recent A2 unit tests. There are also some typical synoptic questions, with answers, so that you can practise what Edexcel's Chief Examiner calls 'joined-up thinking'. Do not treat the answers as model answers or as rubber-stamp responses to be reproduced without thought. The most important reason for studying chemistry is to *understand* it, not merely to repeat it parrot-fashion — you have to do more than simply aim for a good grade.

In some instances, the difference between an A-grade response and a C-grade response has been suggested. To use this section effectively, you should *first answer the questions yourself* and then check your answers against the ones in this book.

Note that, especially in calculations, consequential marking is used. This means that if a mistake is made early in the response, only 1 mark is lost — *provided that all the working is clearly shown* — even though the 'wrong' answer is obtained.

Relative atomic mass values should be obtained from the periodic table on page 84.

Examiner's comments

Candidate responses to long-answer questions are followed by examiner's comments, preceded by the icon *e*. They are interspersed in the answers and indicate where credit is due. They also point out common errors that lower-grade answers are prone to show.

Set 1

Typical synoptic questions

Question 1

(a) The ester 1-propylmethanoate is hydrolysed according to the equation:

$$HCOOCH_2CH_2CH_3 + H_2O \longrightarrow HCOOH + CH_3CH_2CH_2OH$$

Given the following enthalpy of combustion data, calculate the enthalpy of reaction. (3 marks)

Compound	ΔH_c/kJ mol^{-1}
$HCOOCH_2CH_2CH_3$	–2430
H_2O	0
$HCOOH$	–254
$CH_3CH_2CH_2OH$	–2021

(b) The reaction is difficult to perform because the ester is insoluble in water. However, the products *are* soluble in water. Explain why propan-1-ol is water-soluble but 1-propylmethanoate is not. (4 marks)

(c) State the reagent and conditions for the conversion of propan-1-ol into 1-chloropropane. (2 marks)

(d) 1-chloropropane is slowly hydrolysed by aqueous sodium hydroxide solution at room temperature by an S_N2 mechanism. Draw this mechanism. (3 marks)

(e) Given that the C–Cl bond length is 0.18 nm and the C–F bond length is 0.14 nm, explain why the rate of hydrolysis of 1-fluoropropane is too slow to observe at room temperature. (3 marks)

Total: 15 marks

Answer to Question 1

(a) The Hess's law cycle is:

$$HCOOCH_2CH_2CH_3 + H_2O \xrightarrow{\Delta H_r} HCOOH + CH_3CH_2CH_2OH$$

$+5O_2$ (ester + water) ↘ $4CO_2 + 5H_2O$ ↙ $+3O_2$ (acid + alcohol) ✓

ΔH_r + (ΔH_c of acid + ΔH_c of alcohol) = ΔH_c of ester ✓

$\Delta H_r = -2430 - \{-254 + (-2021)\} = -155\ \text{kJ mol}^{-1}$ ✓

The safest way to do these calculations is to draw a labelled Hess's law cycle. Never quote 'ΔH_r = products – reactants', especially if, as here, you are given combustion data, as such a method will give the wrong sign.

(b) The alcohol is covalently bonded and has both a δ+ hydrogen atom and a δ– oxygen atom ✓. It can form hydrogen bonds with the δ– oxygen and the δ+ hydrogen in the water ✓ and is, therefore, water-soluble. The covalent ester is not able to hydrogen-bond with the δ– O in the water ✓ because it does not contain a δ+ hydrogen atom ✓.

Explanations of the solubility of covalent substances in water must indicate which atoms form hydrogen bonds. C-grade answers might simply state that hydrogen bonding is possible between the alcohol and water and not possible between the ester and water, without explaining why.

(c) The reagent for the conversion of an alcohol to a chloroalkane is phosphorus(V) chloride, PCl_5 ✓. The conditions are dry at room temperature ✓.

(d) The mechanism is:

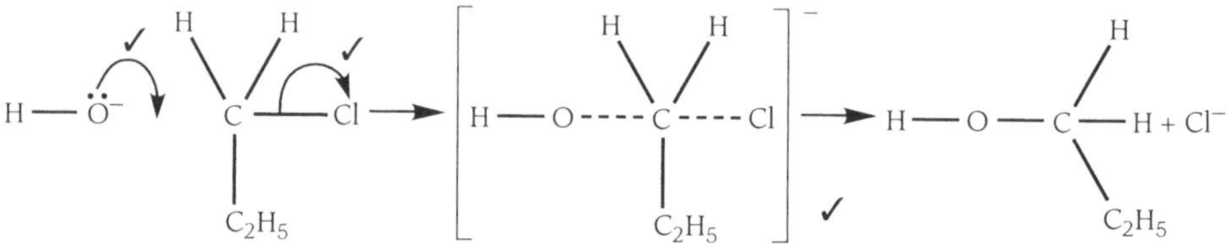

$$H{-}\ddot{O}^{-} + CH(H)(C_2H_5){-}Cl \rightarrow [H{-}O\cdots C(H)(H)(C_2H_5)\cdots Cl]^{-} \rightarrow H{-}O{-}C(H)(H)(C_2H_5) + Cl^{-}$$

✓ ✓ ✓

Make sure that the curly arrow starts from the oxygen atom and not from the minus sign. Don't forget the minus sign on the transition state that has two partial (dotted) bonds.

(e) The C–F bond is shorter than the C–Cl bond and it is therefore stronger ✓. This means that the activation enthalpy for the hydrolysis of the fluoroalkane will be higher ✓, the reaction much slower ✓ and hence unlikely to be observed.

C-grade answers often omit a reference to the increased activation enthalpy.

Question 2

Fluorine reacts with all metals to form ionic compounds and with almost all non-metals to form covalent compounds.

(a) Explain why the boiling temperature of hydrogen fluoride (HF) is higher than that of hydrogen chloride (HCl), but the boiling temperature of carbon tetrafluoride (CF_4) is lower than that of carbon tetrachloride (CCl_4). (8 marks)

(b) Explain the trend in lattice energies of the following ionic substances:

Substance	Radius of cation/nm	Lattice energy/kJ mol^{-1}
RbF	0.15	–770
SrF_2	0.11	–2480
InF_3	0.081	–5690
SnF_4	0.071	–9710

(3 marks)

(c) The enthalpy of formation of solid ionic tin(II) fluoride is −405 kJ mol^{-1}. Use the data below to calculate the enthalpy of formation of SnF_4.

	ΔH/kJ mol^{-1}
First ionisation energy of tin	+710
Second ionisation energy of tin	+1410
Third ionisation energy of tin	+2940
Fourth ionisation energy of tin	+3930
ΔH_a of tin	+79
ΔH_a of fluorine	+301
Lattice energy of SnF_4	−9710
Electron affinity of fluorine	−348

Hence, calculate the enthalpy of the reaction below and comment on its feasibility.

$SnF_4(s) \longrightarrow SnF_2(s) + F_2(g)$ (4 marks)

(d) The solubility of the group 1 fluorides (LiF, NaF, KF, RbF and CsF) increases as the group is descended. Explain this trend. (5 marks)

Total: 20 marks

Answer to Question 2

(a) In hydrogen fluoride, there is hydrogen bonding ✓ between the δ+ hydrogen atom in one molecule and the δ− fluorine atom in another molecule ✓. In hydrogen chloride, there is no hydrogen bonding because the chlorine atom is too big ✓. The intermolecular forces are the weaker induced dipole–induced dipole forces ✓ and so less energy is required ✓ to separate HCl molecules. Therefore, the boiling temperature is lower. In both tetrahalides, the intermolecular forces are induced dipole–induced dipole ✓. Those between CCl_4 molecules are stronger than those between CF_4 molecules ✓ because there are more electrons in CCl_4 than in CF_4 ✓.

e C-grade answers often fail to explain why hydrogen chloride molecules cannot hydrogen bond with each other. Another omission is the failure to relate weaker forces to less energy required for the separation of the molecules.

(b) The lattice energies become more exothermic across the period (Rb to Sn) because the ions become smaller ✓ and the charge on the cation increases from +1 to +4 ✓. Both factors cause an increase in the strength of the force ✓ between the cation and the anion and hence a more exothermic lattice energy.

e You must understand that the lattice energy depends upon the charge on the ions, and inversely on the sum of the radii of the cation and anion.

(c) $\Delta H_f = +79 + 710 + 1410 + 2940 + 3930 + \{4 \times (301)\} + \{4 \times (-348)\} + (-9710)$
$= -829$ kJ mol^{-1} ✓✓

Therefore, for the reaction:

$$SnF_4(s) \longrightarrow SnF_2(s) + F_2(g)$$

$$\Delta H_r = \Delta H_f \text{ of } SnF_2 + \Delta H_f \text{ of } F_2 - \Delta H_f \text{ of } SnF_4$$

$$= -405 + 0 - (-829) = +424\,kJ\,mol^{-1}$$ ✓

which is positive. Therefore, the reaction is not likely to occur ✓.

Don't forget that ΔH_f of an element in its standard state is zero.

(d) ΔH_{soln} = –lattice energy + ΔH_{hyd} of cation + ΔH_{hyd} of anion ✓

As the group is descended, the radii of the cations become larger ✓. This means that the lattice energy *and* the hydration enthalpy of the cation decrease ✓. However, the lattice energy depends upon the sum of the radii of the cation and anion. The fluoride ion is small, so the lattice energy decreases more than the hydration enthalpy ✓. Therefore, ΔH_{soln} becomes less endothermic ✓ and the fluorides become more soluble.

ΔH_{soln} is determined by the enthalpy required to break up the lattice into gaseous ions and that released when these ions are hydrated.

■ ■ ■

Question 3

(a) When hydroxyethanoic acid, $HOCH_2COOH$, is heated at low pressure, it reversibly forms a cyclic ester, $C_4H_4O_4$, and water.

$$2HOCH_2COOH(g) \rightleftharpoons C_4H_4O_4(g) + 2H_2O(g) \quad \Delta H = +17\,kJ\,mol^{-1}$$

When heated to 170°C in a vessel at a pressure of 0.25 atm, 46% of the hydroxyethanoic acid reacts. Calculate the value of K_p. (6 marks)

(b) State and explain the effect on the value of K_p and on the position of equilibrium of:

(i) an increase in temperature (3 marks)

(ii) an increase in pressure (3 marks)

(c) Given that the enthalpy of formation of hydroxyethanoic acid is –540 kJ mol^{-1} and the enthalpy of formation of $H_2O(g)$ is –242 kJ mol^{-1}, calculate the ΔH_f of the cyclic ester. (4 marks)

(d) Hydroxyethanoic acid is a weak acid with pK_a = 3.83. Calculate the pH of the buffer solution made by adding 4.90 g of sodium hydroxyethanoate (molar mass = 98.0 g mol^{-1}) to 100 cm^3 of 0.844 mol dm^{-3} hydroxyethanoic acid. (5 marks)

Total: 21 marks

Answer to Question 3

(a) Assume that the initial amount of hydroxyethanoic acid is 1 mol.

	$2HOCH_2COOH$	$C_4H_4O_4$	$2H_2O$
Initial moles	1	0	0
Change	−0.46	$+\frac{1}{2} \times 0.46$	+0.46 ✓
Moles at equilibrium	1 − 0.46 = 0.54	0.23	0.46
Mole fraction	$\frac{0.54}{1.23} = 0.439$	$\frac{0.23}{1.23} = 0.187$	$\frac{0.46}{1.23} = 0.374$ ✓
Partial pressure/atm	0.439 × 0.25 = 0.110	0.187 × 0.25 = 0.0468	0.374 × 0.25 = 0.0935 ✓

Total moles at equilibrium = 1.23 ✓

$$K_p = \frac{p(C_4H_4O_4) \times p(H_2O)^2}{p(HOCH_2COOH)^2} \checkmark = \frac{0.0468 \times (0.0935)^2}{(0.110)^2} = 0.0338\,\text{mol dm}^{-3} \checkmark$$

Remember to use the stoichiometry of the equation. For every mole of acid that reacts, $\frac{1}{2}$ mole of cyclic ester is produced. The total number of moles at equilibrium must be calculated and used to find the mole fractions, which are then multiplied by the total pressure to give the partial pressures. Don't forget to give the expression for K_p and its units.

(b) (i) As the reaction is endothermic ✓, an increase in temperature causes the value of K_p to rise ✓. Hence, the equilibrium position shifts to the right ✓.

(ii) An increase in pressure has no effect on the value of K_p ✓. However, because there are 3 mol of gas on the right-hand side of the equation and only 2 mol of gas on the left ✓, the increase in pressure causes the equilibrium position to shift to the left ✓ (towards the side with fewer gas molecules).

The correct explanation is that the equilibrium shifts to the right because the value of K_p increases, and not that the equilibrium shifts to the right because of Le Châtelier and therefore the value of K_p also increases. Always explain the effect of pressure on the position of equilibrium in terms of the number of gas moles on each side of the equation and not in terms of volumes. Do not say that an increase of temperature or pressure 'favours' a particular direction, as both increases will increase the rates of the forward and the back reactions.

(c) The Hess's law cycle is:

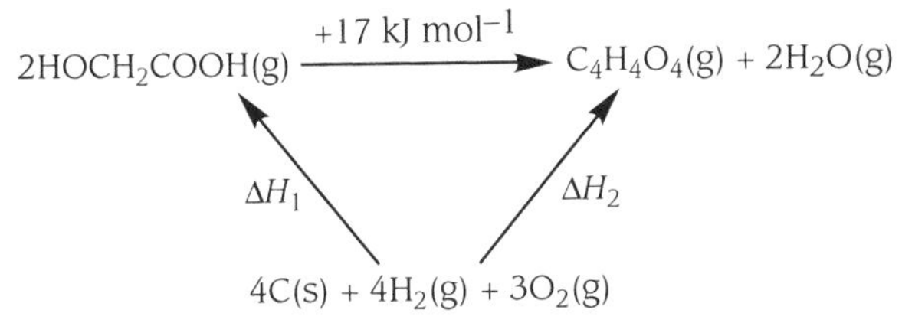

where $\Delta H_1 = 2 \times \Delta H_f$ of hydroxyethanoic acid and $\Delta H_2 = \Delta H_f$ of $C_4H_4O_4 + 2 \times \Delta H_f$ of water ✓.

$\Delta H_2 = \Delta H_1 + (+17)$ ✓
ΔH_f of $C_4H_4O_4 + 2 \times (-242) = 2 \times (-540) + 17$ ✓
ΔH_f of $C_4H_4O_4 = -1080 + 17 - (-484) = -579\,kJ\,mol^{-1}$ ✓

Usually you are asked to calculate ΔH_r from ΔH_f values. This question is slightly different, but the theory (Hess's law) is the same. Don't forget to multiply the values of ΔH_f of hydroxyethanoic acid and water by two, as there are two moles of each in the equation.

(d) Volume of solution is $100\,cm^3 = 0.100\,dm^3$.

$$\text{Amount of salt} = \frac{4.90\,g}{98\,g\,mol^{-1}} = 0.0500\,mol$$

$$[\text{salt}] = \frac{0.0500\,mol}{0.100\,dm^3} = 0.500\,mol\,dm^{-3}$$ ✓

$[\text{acid}] = 0.844\,mol\,dm^{-3}$

$K_a = 10^{-pK_a} = 10^{-3.83} = 1.48 \times 10^{-4}\,mol\,dm^{-3}$ ✓

$$K_a = \frac{[H^+][\text{salt}]}{[\text{acid}]}$$ ✓

$$[H^+] = \frac{K_a[\text{acid}]}{[\text{salt}]} = \frac{1.48 \times 10^{-4} \times 0.844}{0.500} = 2.50 \times 10^{-4}$$ ✓

$pH = -\log_{10}[H^+] = 3.60$ ✓

You must calculate the concentration of the salt, and then substitute it into the expression for K_a, which you must state. This and the incorrect calculation of K_a from pK_a are common errors. Don't forget to give the pH to two decimal places.

Question 4

(a) (i) Draw 'dot-and-cross' diagrams to show the electronic structure of molecules of both ammonia and sulphur trioxide. Hence deduce their shape and suggest values for the H–N–H and the O=S=O bond angles in these molecules. (6 marks)

(ii) The boiling temperatures of the group 5 hydrides are given in the table.

Hydride	Boiling temperature/K
Ammonia, NH_3	240
Phosphine, PH_3	183
Arsine, AsH_3	218
Stibine, SbH_3	256

Explain the variation in the boiling temperatures. (5 marks)

(b) (i) Ammonia is a weak base.

$$NH_3 + H_2O \rightleftharpoons NH_4^+ + OH^-$$

An aqueous solution of ammonia has a pH of 11.73. Calculate the concentration of hydroxide ions in the solution. (3 marks)

(ii) Ammonium ions, NH_4^+, can be oxidised to nitrogen and hydrogen ions. Deduce the ionic half-equation for this oxidation. (1 mark)

(iii) Theoretically, in acid solution, VO_2^+ ions (which contain vanadium in the +5 state) will oxidise ammonium ions to nitrogen and hydrogen ions. The half-equation for the reduction of VO_2^+(aq) is:

$$VO_2^+(aq) + 2H^+(aq) + e^- \longrightarrow VO^{2+}(aq) + H_2O(l) \quad E^\ominus = +1.00\text{ V}$$

Write the overall ionic equation for this reaction. (2 marks)

(iv) The standard electrode potential for the overall reaction is given by:

$$E^\ominus_{cell} = +0.73\text{ V}$$

Calculate the value of $E^\ominus$ for the reaction that you wrote for (ii). (2 marks)

(v) In practice, this reaction is not observed. Suggest why this is so. (2 marks)

Total: 21 marks

Answer to Question 4

(a) (i)

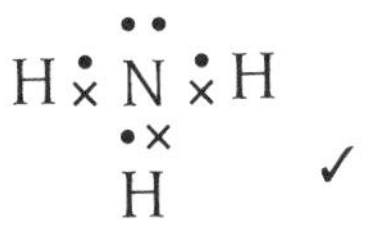

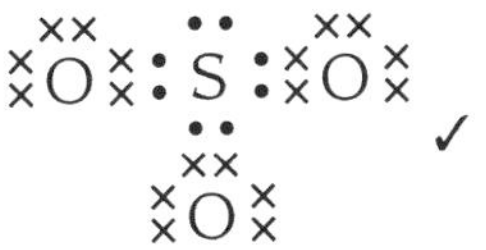

```
    ••
H ×• N •× H
    •×
     H        ✓

 ××     ••     ××
×O×× : S : ××O×
 ××     ••     ××
        ××
       ×O×
        ××        ✓
```

Ammonia has three bond pairs and one lone pair ✓. Therefore, its shape is pyramidal, with an H–N–H bond angle of 107° ✓.

Sulphur trioxide has three σ-bond pairs and no lone pairs ✓. Therefore, it is trigonal planar, with a bond angle of 120° ✓.

C-grade answers often omit the lone pairs of electrons on the oxygen atoms, and state, rather than deduce, the shapes of the molecules. Remember that *deduce* means *give an explanation*. The shapes are determined by the repulsion of electron pairs and not by the repulsion of atoms or bonds — another common error.

(ii) The general trend of boiling temperature from PH_3 to SbH_3 is upwards, but ammonia does not fit this trend. There are hydrogen bonds between ammonia molecules ✓. These are stronger than the van der Waals forces between phosphine molecules ✓. Therefore, more energy is needed to separate ammonia molecules ✓ and so it has a higher boiling temperature than phosphine.

The strongest forces between the molecules of the other hydrides are instantaneous induced dipole–induced dipole (dispersion) forces ✓. The strength of these forces depends on the number of electrons in the molecule ✓, so the strength and the boiling temperatures increase from phosphine to stibine.

The substance with the highest boiling temperature is stibine, SbH_4. Although it does not hydrogen bond, its induced dipole–induced dipole forces are even stronger than the hydrogen bonds between ammonia molecules. This is because stibine has so many electrons and ammonia's hydrogen bonds are fairly weak. (They are weaker than those in water, as the electronegativity difference between N and H is much less than that between O and H.)

(b) (i) $[H^+] = 10^{-pH} = 10^{-11.73} = 1.86 \times 10^{-12}$ mol dm^{-3} ✓

$[OH^-] = \frac{1 \times 10^{-14}}{[H^+]}$ ✓ $= \frac{1 \times 10^{-14}}{1.86 \times 10^{-12}}$

$= 0.0054$ mol dm^{-3} ✓

or

$pOH = 14 - pH = 14 - 11.73 = 2.27$ ✓

$[OH^-] = 10^{-pOH}$ ✓ $= 10^{-2.27} = 0.0054$ mol dm^{-3} ✓

The concentration should be given to two significant figures, because the pH is given to two decimal places.

(ii) $2NH_4^+(aq) \longrightarrow N_2(g) + 8H^+(aq) + 6e^-$ ✓

Make sure that your half-equations always balance for charge. Here, each side is +2. The number of electrons will equal the change in oxidation number (here $2 \times (-3)$ to $0 = 6$). As the oxidation number of nitrogen in the NH_4^+ ion is going up, it is being oxidised and so the electrons are on the right of the equation (oxidation is loss — OILRIG).

(iii) Multiplying the given equation by 6 and adding the result to the equation in (ii) ✓ gives:

$6VO_2^+(aq) + 12H^+(aq) + 6e^- \longrightarrow 6VO^{2+}(aq) + 6H_2O(l)$

$2NH_4^+(aq) \longrightarrow N_2(g) + 8H^+(aq) + 6e^-$

$6VO_2^+(aq) + 2NH_4^+(aq) + 4H^+(aq) \longrightarrow 6VO^{2+}(aq) + 6H_2O(l) + N_2(g)$ ✓

The number of electrons in both half-equations must be the same, so vanadium's equation must be multiplied by 6. As the NH_4^+ half-equation is written as an oxidation and the VO_2^+ equation as a reduction, neither equation needs reversing as the electrons will cancel on addition.

(iv) $6VO_2^+(aq) + 12H^+(aq) + 6e^- \longrightarrow 6VO^{2+}(aq) + 6H_2O(l) \quad E^\ominus = +1.00$ V

$2NH_4^+(aq) \longrightarrow N_2(g) + 8H^+(aq) + 6e^- \quad E^\ominus = x$

$E^\ominus_{cell} = +1.00 + x = +0.73$ V ✓

$x = E^\ominus$ of half-equation in (ii) $= +0.73 - (+1.00) = -0.27$ V ✓

$E^\ominus$ cell is the sum of the $E^\ominus$ values of the oxidation and reduction half-equations.

(v) Although the reaction is thermodynamically feasible ($E^\ominus_{cell}$ positive), the activation energy is too high ✓, and hence the reaction is too slow to be observed ✓.

This is an example of when a reaction is thermodynamically unstable, but kinetically stable.

Unit Test 6B, June 2003

Section A

This question is *compulsory*.

Question 1

A sample of ammonia was dissolved in water to produce 100 cm^3 of solution X. 10.0 cm^3 of solution X was made up to a volume of 250 cm^3, and 25.0 cm^3 of this diluted ammonia solution was then titrated with aqueous hydrochloric acid of concentration 0.110 mol dm^{-3}. 37.10 cm^3 of the acid was required to neutralise the ammonia solution.

(a) Write an equation for the reaction between ammonia and hydrochloric acid, and calculate the number of moles of ammonia in solution X. Calculate the concentration of solution X in mol dm^{-3}. (5 marks)

(b) The above titration was repeated, but this time the pH was measured throughout, until a total of 50.0 cm^3 of aqueous hydrochloric acid had been added. Carefully sketch the pH curve that you would expect for this titration. Name an indicator suitable for the titration and use the curve to justify your choice. (7 marks)

(c) Suggest a chemical test to confirm the presence of ammonia in solution X. (2 marks)

Total: 14 marks

Answer to Question 1

(a) $NH_3 + HCl \longrightarrow NH_4Cl$ ✓

Amount of HCl in titration = 0.110 mol dm^{-3} × 0.0371 dm^3 = 0.004081 mol ✓

As the ratio of NH_3 to HCl is 1:1, the amount of ammonia in a 25 cm^3 sample is 0.004081 mol.

Amount of ammonia in 250 cm^3 of diluted solution = 10 × 0.004081 = 0.04081 mol ✓

Amount of ammonia in 10 cm^3 of solution X = 0.04081 mol

Amount of ammonia in 100 cm^3 of solution X = 10 × 0.04081 = 0.4081 mol ✓

Concentration of ammonia in solution X $= \dfrac{\text{moles}}{\text{volume in dm}^3} = \dfrac{0.4081}{0.100} = 4.08 \text{ mol dm}^{-1}$ ✓

Ammonia is a base and so the reaction is

acid + base ⟶ salt

To do this calculation, you must be clear about what is happening. 10 cm^3 (one-tenth) of solution X is taken and diluted to 250 cm^3. Dilution does not alter the number of moles. One-tenth of this diluted solution is then titrated. The processes in the calculation are:

- volume of acid ⟶ moles of acid

- moles of acid ⟶ moles of ammonia in 25 cm^3 ⟶ moles of ammonia in 250 cm^3 (This came from 10 cm^3 of solution X, so 100 cm^3 of solution X contains ten times more moles of ammonia.)
- moles of ammonia in 100 cm^3 of solution X ⟶ concentration of ammonia

(b)

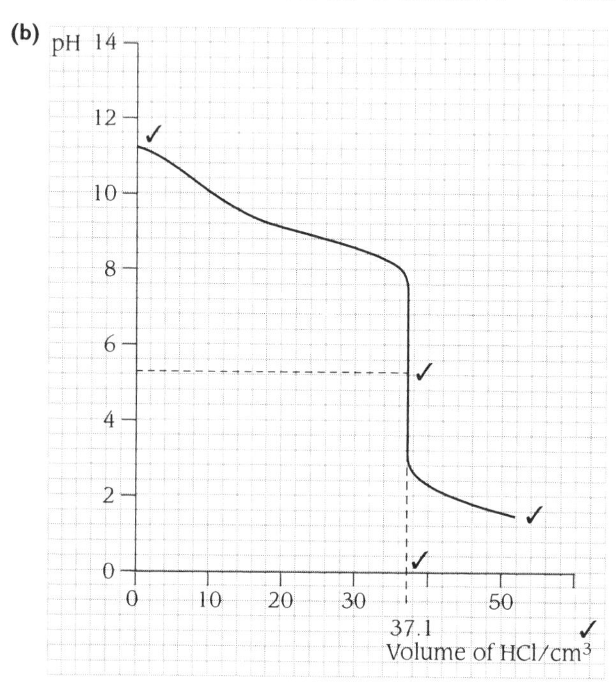

A suitable indicator for this reaction would be methyl orange ✓ because it changes colour completely *within* the pH of the vertical part of the curve ✓.

The marks for this graph are for:

- properly labelled axes, with linear scales of pH on the *y*-axis and volume of HCl/cm^3 on the *x*-axis
- the pH at zero HCl being between 9 and 12
- the graph having a vertical section at 37.1 cm^3 of acid
- the pH halfway up the vertical part being equal to 5, and the vertical part going from a pH of just below 3 to a pH of just above 7
- the pH after 50 cm^3 of acid added tailing off to a value of between 1 and 2

A C-grade answer might draw the pH curve as if alkali had been added to the acid with an end point volume of 25 cm^3. Other common errors might include having the end point pH at 7, or having far too big a pH jump in the vertical part of the graph. A C-grade candidate might give the reason for the choice of indicator to be a colour change at the end point pH, or that its pK_{ind} value is in the vertical part of the graph. In fact, $pK_{ind} \pm 1$ must be in the vertical part.

(c) Add excess of the ammonia solution to a solution of copper(II) sulphate ✓. A deep blue solution would be obtained ✓.

A common C-grade response might be to test the vapours from solution X with damp red litmus paper. Ammonia would turn it blue, but so would amines such as ethylamine and so this answer would not score.

Section B

Answer *two* of the three questions.

Question 2

(a) (i) A fluoride of phosphorus, Y, contains 24.6% by mass of phosphorus and has a molar mass of 126 g mol^{-1}. Deduce the molecular formula of Y. (4 marks)

(ii) Draw the shape of a molecule of compound Y. Show the values of the bond angles on the diagram. (3 marks)

(iii) Compound Y was converted into the ion PF_6^-. Draw and name the shape of PF_6^- and suggest a value for the bond angles. (3 marks)

(b) Consider the following data, which show the formulae and boiling temperatures of the group 7 hydrides.

Hydride	Boiling temperature/°C
HF	19
HCl	–85
HBr	–68
HI	–35

Suggest why hydrogen fluoride, HF, has the highest boiling temperature of the group 7 hydrides. (3 marks)

(c) When hydrogen fluoride is dissolved in water, a weakly acidic solution is formed. Write the expression for the acid dissociation constant, K_a, for hydrogen fluoride. Calculate the value of K_a, with units, given that a 0.150 mol dm^{-3} solution of hydrogen fluoride has a pH of 2.04. (5 marks)

Total: 18 marks

Answer to Question 2

(a) (i)

Element	Composition/%	% divided by A_r ✓	Divide by smallest
Phosphorus	24.6	$\frac{24.6}{31} = 0.794$	$\frac{0.794}{0.794} = 1$
Fluorine	75.4	$\frac{75.4}{19} = 3.97$ ✓	$\frac{3.97}{0.794} = 5$

Therefore, the empirical formula is PF_5 ✓.

$(31 \times 1) + (19 \times 5) = 126$ = molar mass ✓

So the molecular formula is also PF_5 ✓.

You must show clearly that the molecular and empirical formulae are the same.

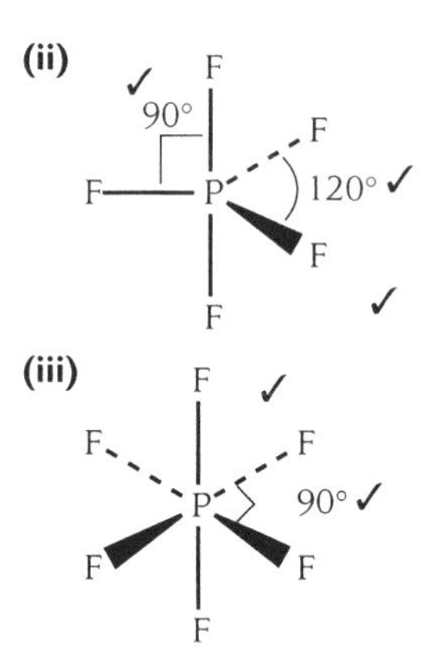

The shape is octahedral ✓.

Your diagrams must show that the structures are three-dimensional. The angles *must* be marked on the diagram in (ii) and (iii) and the shape *must* be named in (iii). Many C-grade candidates might fail to do this.

(b) Hydrogen fluoride has hydrogen bonding (as well as induced dipole–induced dipole forces) between its molecules ✓. The halogen atoms in the other hydrides are too large to form hydrogen bonds ✓. They only have the weaker induced dipole–induced dipole forces. Therefore, more energy is required to separate the hydrogen fluoride molecules than to separate the molecules of the other hydrides ✓. This means that hydrogen fluoride has the highest boiling temperature.

You must make it clear that hydrogen bonds are intermolecular forces. The strength of the covalent bonds has nothing to do with boiling and so must not be mentioned. You must also say why the other hydrides do not form hydrogen bonds. C-grade candidates might fail to make any comparison with the other group 7 hydrides or fail to relate the strength of the intermolecular force to the energy required to overcome it.

(c) $K_a = \frac{[H^+][F^-]}{[HF]}$ ✓

As the pH = 2.04,

$[H^+] = 10^{-2.04} = 0.00912\ mol\,dm^{-3}$ ✓

Every mole of HF that ionises produces an equal number of moles of H^+ and F^-, so $[H^+] = [F^-]$ ✓.

$$K_a = \frac{[H^+]^2}{[HF]} = \frac{(0.00912)^2}{0.150} = 5.55 \times 10^{-4}$$ ✓ $mol\,dm^{-3}$ ✓

A more accurate answer would take into account that [HF] = (0.150 – the amount that ionised). So [HF] = (0.150 – 0.00912) = 0.141 $mol\,dm^{-3}$. This gives a value of $K_a = 5.90 \times 10^{-4}\ mol\,dm^{-3}$.

Question 3

(a) A compound, Z, of formula $C_6H_5C(CH_3)(CN)OCOCH_3$, has been proposed as a possible new insecticide. Consider the following scheme for the production of compound Z from benzene.

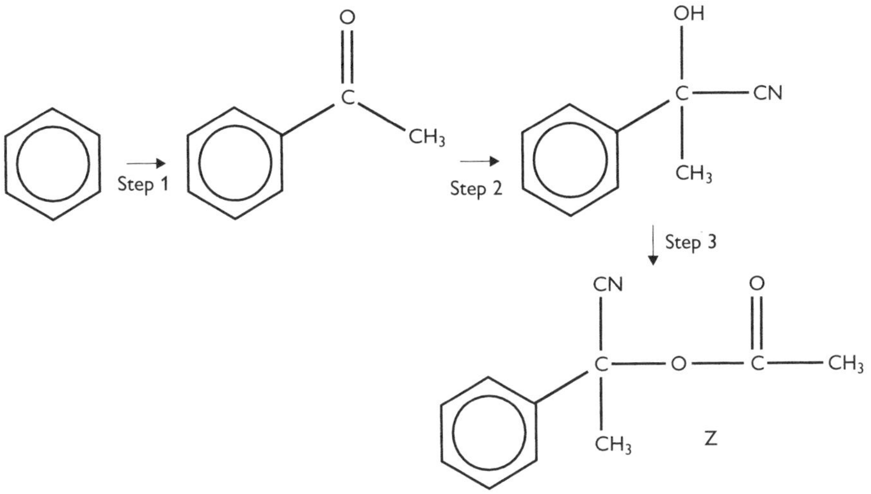

Step 1 → Step 2 → Step 3 → Z

(i) Steps 1 and 3 both use the same reagent but under different conditions. Identify this reagent and state the difference in the conditions under which the reactions are carried out. (3 marks)

(ii) Give the reagents for step 2, and draw and name the mechanism. (5 marks)

(iii) In an experiment, 3.00 g of compound Z was produced from 10.0 g of benzene, C_6H_6. Calculate the percentage yield of compound Z. Give a reason why the yield was so low. (5 marks)

(b) Urea, $CO(NH_2)_2$, and ammonium sulphate, $(NH_4)_2SO_4$, can be used as fertilisers.

(i) Urea can be leached out of the soil by rainwater, because it is soluble in water. Suggest why you would expect urea to be soluble in water. (3 marks)

(ii) Suggest *two* disadvantages of using ammonium sulphate, $(NH_4)_2SO_4$, as a fertiliser. (2 marks)

Total: 18 marks

Answers to question 3

(a) (i) Ethanoyl chloride, CH_3COCl ✓

For step 1, a catalyst of anhydrous aluminium chloride ✓ is needed under dry conditions (and it needs heating under reflux). Step 3 also needs to be in dry conditions but it does not need a catalyst ✓ (and works at room temperature).

C-grade answers might fail to emphasise that the aluminium chloride must be anhydrous. Although step 3 is an esterification reaction, concentrated sulphuric acid is not needed as the reaction between an alcohol and an acid chloride is rapid at room temperature.

(ii) Hydrogen cyanide with a trace of sodium hydroxide ✓

$$C_6H_5C(CH_3)=O + (:CN)^- \rightarrow C_6H_5C(CH_3)(CN)-O^- \quad H-CN$$

$$\downarrow$$

$$C_6H_5C(CH_3)(CN)-OH + :CN^-$$

The mechanism is nucleophilic addition ✓.

There must be both CN^- ions (for the first step in the mechanism) and HCN molecules (for the last step). Make sure that the curly arrow goes from the C of the CN^- ion towards the C of the C=O group, and that an arrow goes from the π-bond to the O of the C=O group. The intermediate must be charged. The arrow must go from the O atom, not from the minus sign, towards the H of the HCN molecule. C-grade candidates might forget to name the type of reaction. Make sure that you answer the question fully.

(iii) Amount of benzene $= \dfrac{10.0\,\text{g}}{78\,\text{g mol}^{-1}} = 0.128\,\text{mol}$ ✓

Theoretical amount of Z possible = 0.128 mol as the reactants have a 1:1 ratio ✓.
Theoretical mass of Z (theoretical yield) $= 0.128\,\text{mol} \times 189\,\text{g mol}^{-1} = 24.2\,\text{g}$ ✓

$$\text{percentage yield} = \frac{\text{actual yield}}{\text{theoretical yield}} \times 100 = \frac{3.00\,\text{g}}{24.2\,\text{g}} \times 100 = 12.4\%$$ ✓

This is very low because there are three steps to the reaction and side reactions decrease the yield at each step ✓.

C-grade answers might fail to state that the reaction has a 1:1 ratio. The worst answers might state that the percentage yield is (mass produced × 100)/(mass to start with), which would score zero.

(b) (i) Nitrogen and oxygen are highly electronegative. Urea has four δ+ hydrogen atoms as well as δ– oxygen and nitrogen atoms ✓. Therefore, it is able to form many hydrogen bonds ✓ with the δ– oxygen and δ+ hydrogen atoms in water molecules ✓, and so is very soluble.

If a covalent substance is water-soluble, think about whether it will be able to form hydrogen bonds with water. If so, either describe how these will form or draw a diagram showing the partial charges and the hydrogen bonds.

(ii) It is very soluble and so can be leached out by rainwater ✓. Compared with most other manufactured fertilisers (e.g. urea or ammonium nitrate) it contains a low percentage of nitrogen ✓. It lowers the pH of soil, which may be a disadvantage in certain soils and for certain crops ✓.

Any two of the above three points would score the marks. Don't think that all aquatic life will die if you use this fertiliser. Only huge overuse causes problems such as eutrophication, which is mainly due to phosphates, rather than nitrogen compounds. It doesn't cause acid rain, global warming or a hole in the ozone layer!

■ ■ ■

Question 4

(a) Consider the following equilibrium, which illustrates one industrial method used to produce hydrogen:

$$CH_4(g) + 2H_2O(g) \rightleftharpoons CO_2(g) + 4H_2(g)$$

In an experiment, 10 g of methane, CH_4, and 54 g of water, H_2O, were heated in a container of volume 4 dm^3. At equilibrium, 2.0 mol of hydrogen, H_2, had formed. Write an expression for the equilibrium constant K_c for this system, and use the data to calculate a value for K_c, with units. (8 marks)

(b) The following table shows some data for enthalpies of formation, ΔH_f.

Substance	ΔH_f/kJ mol^{-1}
CH_4(g)	−76
H_2O(g)	−242
CO_2(g)	−394

Use these data to calculate the enthalpy change for the reaction in (a). (3 marks)

(c) In practice, the industrial production of hydrogen by this method is conducted at a moderately high pressure of 30 atm and a high temperature of 750°C, in the presence of a nickel catalyst. Suggest why these conditions are used, considering the factors of rate and yield. (7 marks)

Total: 18 marks

Answer to Question 4

(a) $K_c = \dfrac{[CO_2]_{eq}[H_2]^4_{eq}}{[CH_4]_{eq}[H_2O]^2_{eq}}$ ✓

	CH_4	$2H_2O$	CO_2	$4H_2$
Moles at start	$\frac{10\,g}{16\,g\,mol^{-1}} = 0.625$	$\frac{54\,g}{18\,g\,mol^{-1}} = 3.0$ ✓	0	0
Change	$-\frac{1}{4} \times 2 = -0.50$	$-\frac{1}{2} \times 2 = -1.0$	$+\frac{1}{4} \times 2.0 = +0.5$	+2.0
Moles at equilibrium	0.625 – 0.50 = 0.125 ✓	3.0 – 1.0 = 2.0 ✓	0.50 ✓	2.0
Concentration at equilibrium	$\frac{0.125}{4}$ ✓ = 0.03125 mol dm^{-3}	$\frac{2.0}{4} = 0.50$ mol dm^{-3}	$\frac{0.50}{4} = 0.125$ mol dm^{-3}	$\frac{2.0}{4} = 0.50$ mol dm^{-3}

$$K_c = \frac{(0.125\,mol\,dm^{-3})(0.50\,mol\,dm^{-3})^4}{(0.03125\,mol\,dm^{-3})(0.50\,mol\,dm^{-3})^2} = 1.0 ✓ \, mol^2\,dm^{-6} ✓$$

$[H_2O]$ is only omitted if water is the solvent. There is 1 mark for the starting amounts of methane and water. You have to use the stoichiometry of the equation to work out that if 2 mol of H_2 are produced, then $\frac{1}{4}$ of 2 mol of CO_2 is also produced, and also that $\frac{1}{2}$ of 2 mol of water and $\frac{1}{4}$ of 2 mol of methane react. The initial moles of water are 54/18, not 54/(2 × 18). The mole ratio is needed to work out how much water reacted. This, and forgetting to divide the moles at equilibrium by the volume of 4 dm^3, would be common errors in C-grade answers. The weakest candidates would probably use the initial moles of methane and water, divided by 4 dm^3, in their calculation of K_c. It is always a good idea to put the subscript 'eq' in the expression for K to remind you of the necessity of using equilibrium concentrations.

(b) The Hess's law cycle is:

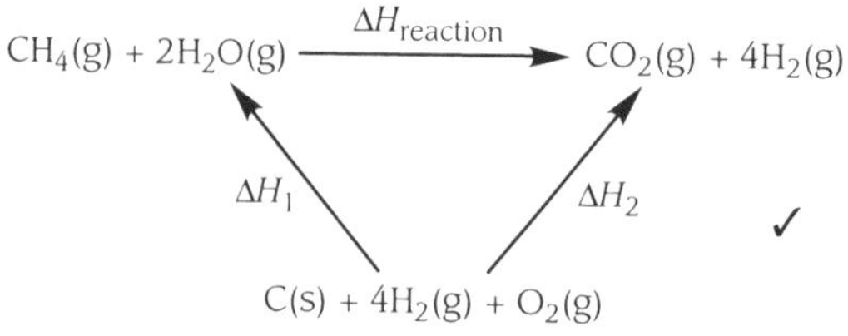

$CH_4(g) + 2H_2O(g) \xrightarrow{\Delta H_{reaction}} CO_2(g) + 4H_2(g)$

ΔH_1 (from $C(s) + 4H_2(g) + O_2(g)$ to $CH_4(g) + 2H_2O(g)$); ΔH_2 (from $C(s) + 4H_2(g) + O_2(g)$ to $CO_2(g) + 4H_2(g)$) ✓

$C(s) + 4H_2(g) + O_2(g)$

$\Delta H_1 = \Delta H_f$ of $CH_4 + 2 \times \Delta H_f$ of $H_2O = -76 + 2 \times (-242) = -560$

$\Delta H_2 = \Delta H_f$ of $CO_2 + 4 \times \Delta H_f$ of $H_2 = -394 + 4 \times 0 = -394$ ✓

$\Delta H_1 + \Delta H_r = \Delta H_2$

$\Delta H_r = \Delta H_2 - \Delta H_1 = -394 - (-560) = +166\,kJ\,mol^{-1}$ ✓

C-grade answers might include the meaningless 'ΔH_r = products – reactants' or the totally wrong '$\Delta H_r = \Delta H_{reactants} - \Delta H_{products}$'. Failure to multiply the ΔH_f of water by two and not realising that the enthalpy of formation of any element is zero are also likely errors.

(c) The nickel catalyst causes the reaction to go via a different route with lower activation energy. This increases the rate of reaction, but does not alter the equilibrium yield ✓.

A high temperature of 750°C is used because the reaction is endothermic ✓. Therefore, a high temperature causes an increase in the value of the equilibrium constant ✓ and an increased equilibrium yield ✓ of hydrogen. The high temperature also causes the rate to increase ✓. However, an even higher temperature, even though it would increase both the rate and the equilibrium yield, would not be economically feasible ✓.

A moderate pressure is used because a higher pressure would drive the equilibrium to the side with fewer gas moles. In this case, that is to the left, which has 3 gas moles as opposed to 5 on the right ✓. Thus, the equilibrium yield of hydrogen would be decreased ✓. Pressure does not affect the rate of this reaction, but a high enough pressure is required to drive the gases through the catalyst ✓ and on to the next stage of manufacture.

e There is 1 mark for the catalyst increasing the rate and then the candidate can score a maximum of 6 marks from the next eight scoring points. The question asks you to consider the factors of rate and yield but not to explain them, so explanations of collision theory are not necessary. Avoid using phrases such as 'favouring the reactants', because the meaning is not clear. C-grade candidates might fail to mention that an increase in temperature results in an increase in the value of the equilibrium constant. There might also be a tendency to state that the temperature choice is a 'compromise between rate and yield', thus confusing this endothermic process with the exothermic Haber process. The catalysed reaction is zero order with respect to the two gaseous reactants. Therefore, an increase in pressure does not alter the rate of the reaction. This is almost always the case with gaseous reagents using a catalyst containing a *d*-block element, such as in this process and in the Haber process, and with enzyme-catalysed reactions.

Unit Test 6B, January 2003

Section A

This question is *compulsory*.

Question 1

Manganate(VII) ions react with ethanedioate ions in acidic solution.

$$2MnO_4^-(aq) + 16H^+(aq) + 5C_2O_4^{2-}(aq) \longrightarrow 2Mn^{2+}(aq) + 8H_2O(l) + 10CO_2(g)$$

(a) In a particular experiment, 200 cm^3 of aqueous potassium manganate(VII), $KMnO_4$, of concentration 0.0500 mol dm^{-3}, was mixed with 50 cm^3 of ethanedioic acid, HOOCCOOH, of concentration 0.500 mol dm^{-3}, and 80 cm^3 of 1.0 mol dm^{-3} sulphuric acid.

(i) Show, by calculation, that the starting concentration of the manganate(VII) ions was 3.03×10^{-2} mol dm^{-3}. (1 mark)

(ii) The concentration of the manganate(VII) ions was determined over a period of time and the data recorded in the table below.

Time/s	Concentration of manganate(VII) ions/ mol dm^{-3}
0	3.03×10^{-2}
400	2.98×10^{-2}
800	2.86×10^{-2}
1200	2.75×10^{-2}
1600	1.90×10^{-2}
2000	7.50×10^{-3}
2400	2.50×10^{-3}

Plot a graph of the concentration of manganate(VII) ions against time. From this graph, determine the initial rate of reaction and the rate at 1600 s. (5 marks)

(b) A second experiment was set up involving the same chemicals in the same concentrations as in experiment 1. However, this time some solid manganese(II) sulphate was dissolved in the ethanedioic acid before the potassium manganate(VII) was poured in. The plot of the concentration of manganate(VII) ions against time is given below.

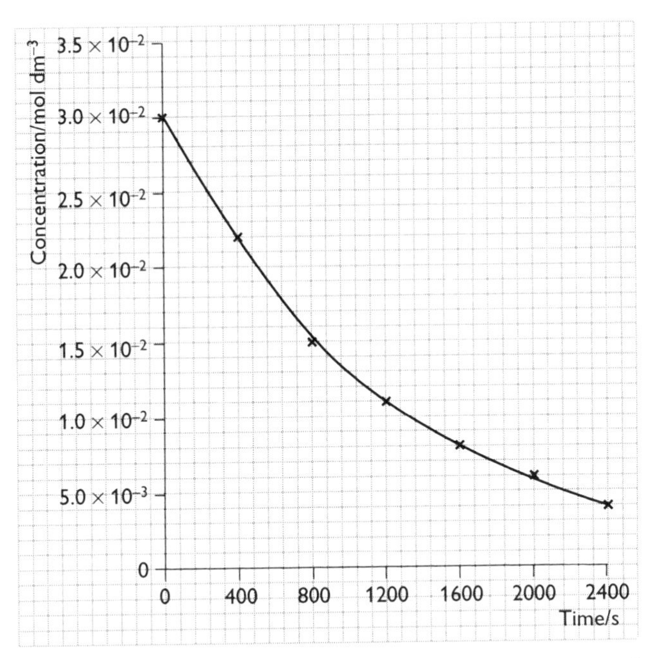

(i) Determine the order of the reaction with respect to manganate(VII) ions by considering the time taken for the concentration to fall by half, using the concentrations at 0, 800 and 1600 s. (3 marks)

(ii) Compare this graph with the one you plotted in (a)(ii). Give two pieces of evidence that manganese(II) sulphate is a catalyst for this reaction. (2 marks)

(c) (i) Carrying out a flame test on potassium manganate(VII) gives a lilac flame. What does this show? (1 mark)

(ii) Describe how aqueous sodium hydroxide solution could be used to show that manganese(II) ions had been produced in the reaction between manganate(VII) ions and ethanedioate ions in acidic solution. (2 marks)

Total: 14 marks

Answer to Question 1

(a) (i) Amount of MnO_4^- ions = $0.0500\,\text{mol dm}^{-3} \times 0.200\,\text{dm}^3 = 0.0100\,\text{mol}$

New volume = $200 + 50 + 80 = 330\,\text{cm}^3 = 0.330\,\text{dm}^3$

Starting concentration of MnO_4^- ions = $\dfrac{0.0100\,\text{mol}}{0.330\,\text{dm}^3} = 3.03 \times 10^{-2}\,\text{mol dm}^{-3}$ ✓

The solution has been diluted by a factor of 330/200, but the safest way to work out the answer is: original volume ⟶ moles taken ⟶ divide by total volume ⟶ final concentration.

(ii)

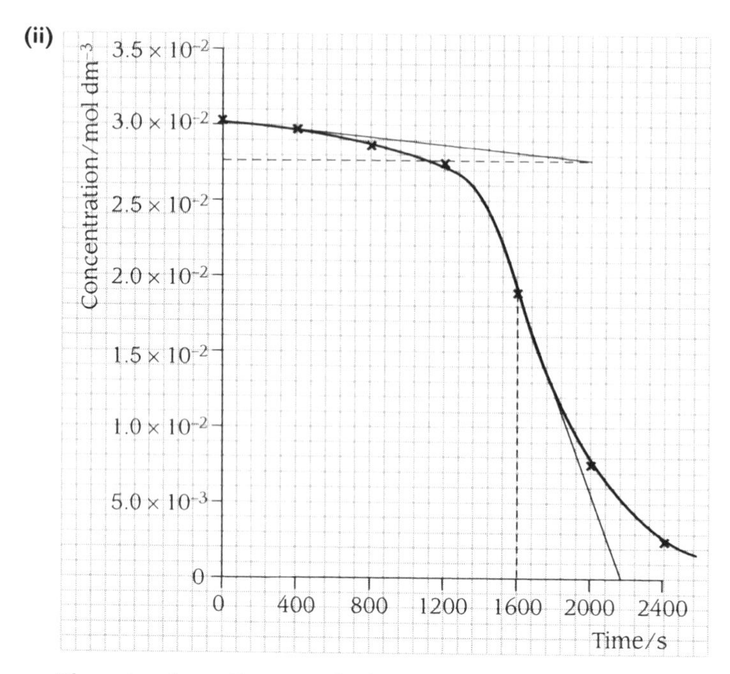

The rate of reaction equals the positive value of the gradient of the line at a particular time.

$$\text{Initial rate} = \frac{(3.03 - 2.78) \times 10^{-2}}{(2000 - 0)} = 1.25 \times 10^{-6}\,\text{mol dm}^{-3}\,\text{s}^{-1}\ ✓$$

$$\text{Rate at 1600 s} = \frac{1.9 \times 10^{-2}}{(2180 - 1600)} = 3.3 \times 10^{-5}\,\text{mol dm}^{-3}\,\text{s}^{-1}\ ✓$$

e On the graph, the marks are for:

- correctly labelled axes with a linear scale ✓
- points correctly plotted ✓
- a smooth curve drawn (C-grade candidates might join up the points, rather than drawing a smooth curve) ✓

Most of this question relies on knowing that the rate of a reaction at a given time can be measured by the gradient (slope) of the graph at that time. You have to draw two tangents and measure their gradients (see pages 14–16 in the Content Guidance section of this guide). An alternative way of working out the *initial* rate is to take the difference in concentration of the first two points ($3.03 \times 10^{-2} - 2.98 \times 10^{-2} = 0.05 \times 10^{-2}$), and divide it by the time elapsed (400 s). This gives a rate of 0.05×10^{-2} mol dm^{-3}/400 s = 1.25×10^{-6} mol dm^{-3} s^{-1}. This method only works for *initial* rates.

(b) (i)

- Time taken for the concentration to halve from 3.0×10^{-2} to 1.5×10^{-2} mol dm^{-3} = 800 s.
- Time taken for the concentration to halve from 1.5×10^{-2} to 7.5×10^{-3} mol dm^{-3} = 900 s.
- Time taken for the concentration to halve from 8.0×10^{-3} to 4.0×10^{-3} mol dm^{-3} = 800 s ✓.

The half-life is constant ✓ (within experimental error), so the reaction is first order ✓ with respect to manganate(VII) ions.

Don't worry about the fact that one half-life is slightly different. This is caused by experimental error. If you had been asked to calculate the half-life, you would have needed to average the three values obtained. Strictly speaking, in this example the only conclusion that can be drawn is that the reaction is first order. Whether it is first order with respect to manganate(VII) ions or ethanedioate ions cannot be deduced from a single experiment.

(ii) The manganese(II) ions must be a catalyst because the second experiment has a steeper slope at the beginning and so its initial rate is greater, even though the concentrations of the reactants are the same ✓. Also, the slope (and hence the rate) in the first experiment increases, as manganese(II) ions are produced ✓.

C-grade candidates would probably score the first point, but might miss the fact that the first experiment is an example of autocatalysis — the catalyst is a product of the reaction.

(c) (i) The lilac colour shows the presence of potassium ions in the compound ✓.

(ii) The presence of Mn^{2+} ions in the product mixture could be shown by adding excess sodium hydroxide ✓. A sandy coloured precipitate ✓, which slowly turns brown, shows the presence of Mn^{2+} ions.

An *excess* of sodium hydroxide is necessary because of the acid present in the reaction mixture.

Section B

Answer two of the three questions.

Question 2

(a) An alcohol, C_3H_8O, was analysed by low-resolution NMR spectroscopy. The spectrum is shown below.

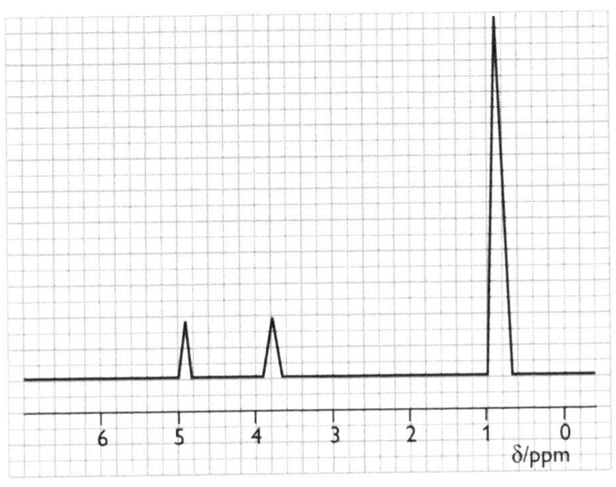

The chemical shifts of some hydrogen nuclei are given in the table below. (R represents an alkyl group.)

Group	δ/ppm
CH_3–R	0.8 to 1.2
R–CH_2–R	1.1 to 1.5
CH–R_3	1.5
R–OH	1.0 to 6.0
R–CH_2OH	3.3 to 4.0
R_2–CH–OH	3.2 to 4.1

Show that the alcohol must be propan-2-ol. (2 marks)

(b) By considering the shapes of the molecules CH_4 and H_2O, explain why a molecule of propan-2-ol has bond angles of approximately 109°, except in the bond C–O–H where the angle is approximately 107°. (4 marks)

(c) Propan-2-ol can be oxidised by an aqueous solution of potassium dichromate(VI) acidified with dilute sulphuric acid. The two half-equations for the reactions involved are:

$$Cr_2O_7^{2-}(aq) + 14H^+(aq) + 6e^- \rightleftharpoons 2Cr^{3+}(aq) + 7H_2O(l)$$
$$C_3H_6O(aq) + 2H^+(aq) + 2e^- \rightleftharpoons C_3H_7OH(aq)$$

(i) Oxidation of the alcohol takes place. Explain what this indicates about the standard electrode potentials of the two half-reactions. Write the equation for the reaction. (3 marks)

(ii) An aqueous solution of chromium(III) ions is coloured. Explain the cause of this colour. (3 marks)

(iii) What would you see when the organic product of the oxidation reaction reacts with iodine in alkaline solution? Write the equation for the reaction. (3 marks)

(d) (i) State the name of the organic product when propan-2-ol is heated with concentrated sulphuric acid. Classify the type of reaction occurring. (2 marks)

(ii) Give the structural formula of the organic product that results from heating propan-2-ol with a mixture of sodium bromide and 50% sulphuric acid. (1 mark)

Total: 18 marks

Answer to Question 2

(a) Propan-2-ol, $CH_3CH(OH)CH_3$, has hydrogen atoms in three different environments. The peak at a chemical shift of 1 is due to the six hydrogen atoms in the two CH_3 groups. The peak at just below 4 is due to the hydrogen atom in the CH group and the peak at 5 is due to the hydroxyl hydrogen atom ✓. The ratio of peak heights is 6:1:1 because there are six CH_3 hydrogen atoms, one CH hydrogen and one OH hydrogen ✓.

Always look for peak heights to identify the *number* of hydrogen atoms and for chemical shifts to identify the *type* of hydrogen atom. The NMR spectrum of propan-1-ol, $CH_3CH_2CH_2OH$, has four peaks due to the four different environments of the hydrogen atoms, with peak heights in the ratio 3:2:2:1.

(b) The shape around an atom is determined by the sum of the number of bond pairs and lone electron pairs around the atom. The electron pairs repel each other to a position of maximum separation ✓. The carbon atoms in both methane and propan-2-ol have four bond pairs and no lone pairs. Therefore, the atoms are arranged tetrahedrally around each carbon atom with a bond angle of 109.5° ✓. The oxygen atoms in both water and propan-2-ol have two bond pairs and two lone pairs, so the atoms joined to the oxygen take up a V-shape with a bond angle of about $104\frac{1}{2}°$ ✓. The smaller bond angle is explained by the fact that lone pairs repel more than bond pairs ✓.

A C-grade answer might not relate methane to the carbon atoms in propan-2-ol, or water to the oxygen atom in the alcohol. Another common error is to describe the repulsion as being between atoms or bonds rather than between pairs of electrons.

(c) (i) For a reaction to be thermodynamically feasible, the value of $E^{\ominus}_{cell}$ must be positive ✓. This means that the standard reduction potential of the dichromate ions must be more positive than that of propanone ✓.

$$Cr_2O_7^{2-}(aq) + 8H^+(aq) + 3C_3H_7OH(aq) \longrightarrow 2Cr^{3+}(aq) + 7H_2O(l) + 3C_3H_6O(aq) ✓$$

The two half-equations are written as reductions, with dichromate ions on the left of the first half-equation and propan-2-ol on the right of the second. C-grade candidates might fail to realise this, and consequently relate the standard reduction potential of dichromate(VI) ions to that of propan-2-ol, rather than propanone. Also, they might miss the first scoring point about $E^{\ominus}_{cell}$ being positive. To obtain the overall equation, the second half-equation has to be multiplied by three and reversed. In this way, the electrons are on opposite sides of the two half-equations and, when the two half-equations are added to find the overall equation, they cancel.

(ii) The six water ligands split the *d*-orbitals into three of lower energy and two of higher energy ✓. When visible light is shone through, light of a certain frequency is absorbed ✓ and an electron is forced from the lower to the upper level ✓ of the split *d*-orbitals.

The colour is due to some of the visible light being *absorbed* by an electron and not due to the emission of coloured light. This is the opposite of the cause of flame colours, in which heat forces an electron into a higher orbital. When the electron falls back to its original orbital, light of a single colour is emitted.

(iii) You would observe a pale yellow precipitate ✓ of iodoform.

$$CH_3COCH_3 + 3I_2 + 4NaOH \longrightarrow CHI_3 + CH_3COONa + 3NaI + 3H_2O ✓✓$$

The iodoform reaction is an example of a reaction in which the carbon chain is shortened by one carbon atom.

(d) (i) Propene ✓ is formed. This is an example of a dehydration ✓ reaction.

(ii) $CH_3CHBrCH_3$ ✓

The mixture produces hydrogen bromide, which is the reactant. 100% sulphuric acid is not used with sodium bromide for two reasons. First, some of the alcohol would be dehydrated as in reaction (d)(i). Second, 100% acid would oxidise much of the hydrogen bromide to bromine.

■ ■ ■

Question 3

(a) Magnesium sulphate is soluble in water, whereas barium sulphate is almost insoluble. Draw an enthalpy level cycle for a group 2 sulphate to show how the lattice energy and enthalpy of hydration can be used to explain the difference in the solubilities of magnesium sulphate and barium sulphate. (4 marks)

(b) Solid magnesium sulphate contains water of crystallisation, $MgSO_4.xH_2O$. 1.23 g of magnesium sulphate crystals were dissolved in distilled water and excess barium nitrate solution was added. The white precipitate of barium sulphate was filtered off, dried and weighed. 1.16 g of anhydrous barium sulphate was formed. Calculate *x*. (5 marks)

(c) State how the thermal stability of magnesium carbonate differs from that of barium carbonate. Account for this difference in terms of the sizes and charges on the cations involved and their polarising power. (4 marks)

(d) (i) Suggest which *d*-block element is most similar to magnesium. Give a reason for your choice. (2 marks)

(ii) *d*-block elements and their compounds are often used in industry as catalysts. Give an example of an industrial process catalysed by a compound of a *d*-block metal. Explain why *d*-block metal compounds have this ability, whereas magnesium compounds do not. (3 marks)

Total: 18 marks

Answer to Question 3

(a)

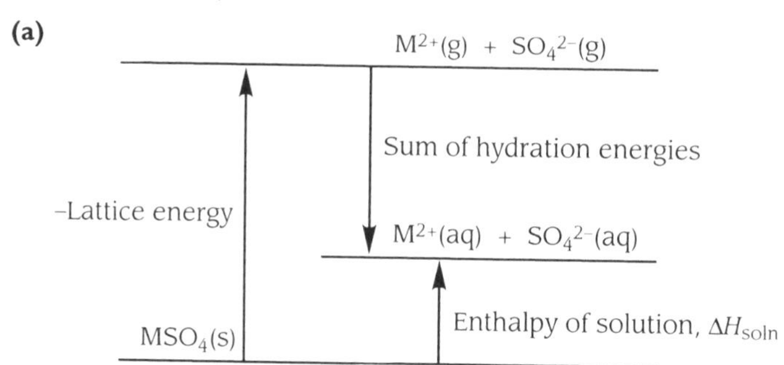

Solubility is determined by the rule that the more endothermic the enthalpy of solution, the less soluble is the ionic solid. From the cycle above, it can be seen that:

ΔH_{soln} = –lattice energy + sum of the hydration energies ✓

As the anion is much larger than the cation, the lattice energy decreases down group 2 to a lesser extent than the hydration energy of the cation. Therefore, the enthalpy of solution of barium sulphate is more endothermic than that of magnesium sulphate. Thus, barium sulphate is less soluble than magnesium sulphate ✓.

e On the enthalpy diagram, there is 1 mark for all species correct, including state symbols, and 1 mark for correctly labelled arrows pointing in the right directions. The diagram must be drawn as an energy level diagram, with the arrows for endothermic processes (–lattice energy and enthalpy of solution) pointing upwards and those for exothermic processes (hydration enthalpies) pointing downwards. C-grade candidates might have the process $MSO_4(s) \longrightarrow M^{2+}(aq) + SO_4^{2-}(aq)$ on a horizontal line. This would be acceptable if a solubility cycle, rather than an energy level cycle, had been required. Solubility is a balance between the endothermic breaking of the lattice and the exothermic hydration of the ions.

(b) Amount of barium sulphate precipitated = 1.16 g/233 g mol^{-1} = 0.00498 mol ✓.
As 1 mol $MgSO_4.xH_2O$ produces 1 mol $BaSO_4$:

amount of $MgSO_4.xH_2O$ = 0.00498 mol ✓

molar mass of $MgSO_4.xH_2O = \dfrac{1.23\,\text{g}}{0.00498\,\text{mol}} = 247\,\text{g mol}^{-1}$ ✓

mass of water in 1 mol of $MgSO_4.xH_2O = 247 - \{24 + 32 + (4 \times 16)\} = 127$ g ✓

$x = \dfrac{127\,\text{g}}{18\,\text{g mol}^{-1}} = 7.05$ mol = 7 to the nearest whole number ✓

e The value of *x* must be a whole number because it is a number of molecules of water. A C-grade answer might leave the value of *x* as 7.05 and would lose a mark. Another route through the calculation is: moles of $BaSO_4$ ⟶ moles of $MgSO_4$ ⟶ mass of anhydrous $MgSO_4$ ⟶ mass of water in 0.00498 mol of $MgSO_4.xH_2O$ ⟶ mass of water in 1 mol of $MgSO_4.xH_2O$ ⟶ moles of water (*x*) in 1 mol of $MgSO_4.xH_2O$.

(c) Magnesium carbonate is less thermally stable than barium carbonate ✓. This is because the ionic radius of Mg^{2+} is less than that of Ba^{2+} ✓ and the charges are the same, so the polarising power of Mg^{2+} is greater than that of Ba^{2+} ✓. This causes a greater distortion of the electron cloud in the carbonate ion ✓ and hence a lower temperature is needed to convert CO_3^{2-} into O^{2-} and $CO_2(g)$.

e The bigger the charge on the cation and the smaller its radius, the greater is its polarising power. The Mg^{2+} ion pulls off an O^{2-} ion from the CO_3^{2-} ion, releasing carbon dioxide gas.

(d) (i) Magnesium is similar to zinc ✓, because neither has coloured compounds, unlike the other *d*-block elements ✓.

An alternative answer is that both have only one oxidation state in their compounds, unlike the other *d*-block elements. Scandium is another *d*-block element similar to magnesium for the same reasons — all its compounds are white and it has only one oxidation state, but its cation is 3+, whereas zinc's is 2+.

(ii) Vanadium(V) oxide catalyses the conversion of sulphur dioxide into sulphur trioxide in the manufacture of sulphuric acid by the contact process ✓. Transition metals do this because they have variable oxidation states ✓. Magnesium compounds cannot be used because magnesium only has a single +2 oxidation state ✓.

In the first step of the contact process, the vanadium(V) oxide oxidises sulphur dioxide to sulphur trioxide and is itself reduced to vanadium(IV) oxide, which then reacts with oxygen to reform vanadium(V) oxide. C-grade candidates might give a metal such as iron in the Haber process as their example. This would not score, because the question asks for an example of catalysis by a *compound* of a *d*-block element. This is an example of how important it is to read the question carefully, and then check to see if your response has answered the question set.

■ ■ ■

Question 4

Compound D, formula $CH_3CH(OH)COOH$, may be prepared from C_3H_7OH by the following series of reactions:

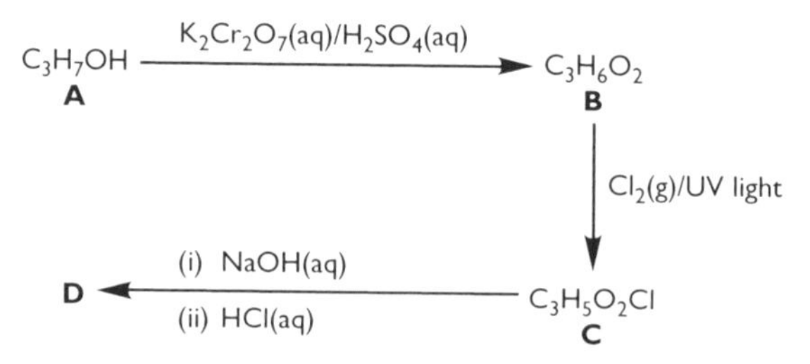

(a) (i) Identify compounds A, B and C. (3 marks)

(ii) Classify the reaction with chlorine. (2 marks)

(iii) D has a boiling temperature of 1860°C, whereas C, $C_3H_5O_2Cl$, boils at 1220°C. Draw a boiling temperature/composition diagram applicable to a mixture of C and D and use it to show how fractional distillation of a mixture of the two compounds could produce a sample of D. (5 marks)

(b) Assuming that the percentage yield for each step in the sequence is 80%, calculate the mass of D that could be made from 60 g of C_3H_7OH. (3 marks)

(c) An aqueous solution of D of concentration 0.100 mol dm^{-3} has a pH value of 2.04.

(i) Calculate the value of the dissociation constant, K_a, for D. (3 marks)

(ii) Suggest, with reasoning, whether D or propanoic acid (CH_3CH_2COOH, $K_a = 1.3 \times 10^{-5}\ mol\ dm^{-3}$) at the same concentration would be more exothermic in reaction with an aqueous sodium hydroxide solution of concentration 0.1 mol dm^{-3}. (2 marks)

Total: 18 marks

Answer to Question 4

(a) (i) A is propan-1-ol, $CH_3CH_2CH_2OH$ ✓
B is propanoic acid, CH_3CH_2COOH ✓
C is 2-chloropropanoic acid, $CH_3CHClCOOH$ ✓

The formula, C_3H_7OH, indicates that A is either propan-1-ol or propan-2-ol. The first step in the reaction series is the oxidation of the alcohol to a carboxylic acid, so A must be a primary alcohol. It cannot be propan-2-ol, which would be oxidised to a ketone. The second step is the substitution of a hydrogen atom by a chlorine atom, and the third step is hydrolysis of the C–Cl bond to C–OH. The alkali needed for this also forms the sodium salt of the acid and so hydrochloric acid is added to reform the COOH group.

(ii) The reaction is free radical ✓ substitution ✓.

The clue to this is the ultraviolet light.

(iii)

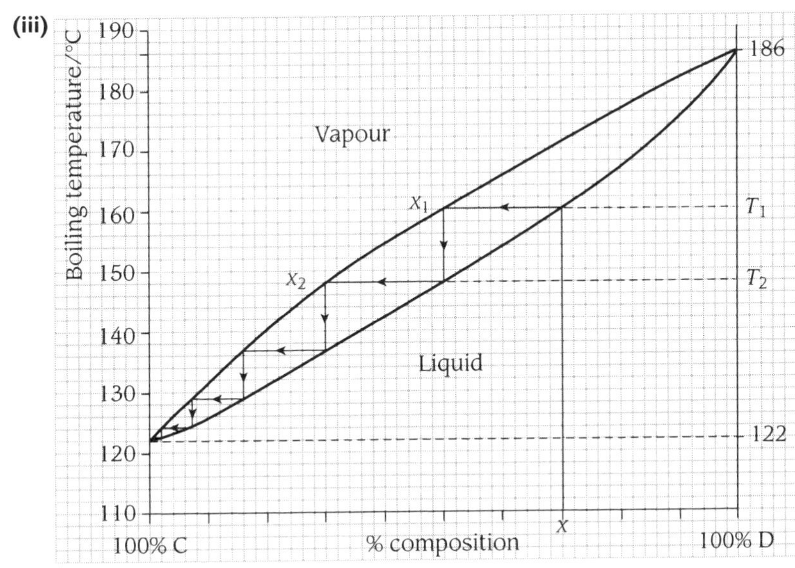

When a liquid of composition x is heated, it boils at a temperature T_1, giving off a vapour x_1, which is richer in the more volatile C ✓. If this is condensed and reboiled, it boils at T_2, producing vapour x_2 and so on until pure vapour C comes out of the top of the column ✓. The remaining liquid gets steadily richer

in the less volatile D, and when all the C has boiled off the top of the column, pure D is left behind ✓.

The diagram marks are awarded for:

- correctly labelled axes, with the boiling points marked ✓
- the liquid and vapour areas being indicated or the lower line marked 'variation of boiling temperature with composition' and the upper line marked 'composition of vapour' ✓

C-grade answers might not have the areas or the lines in the diagram labelled. Also, the tie lines might not have been used in the answer. You must make it clear that you understand that:

- the vapour is richer in the more volatile compound
- the process is one of condensing and reboiling many times, and this is explained by the tie lines
- the vapour that first comes out of the top of the column is pure more-volatile substance and the liquid left behind in the distillation flask is pure less-volatile compound

(b) Amount of C_3H_7OH taken $= \dfrac{60\,\text{g}}{60\,\text{g mol}^{-1}} = 1.0$ mol ✓

After the first step, 0.8×1.0 mol $= 0.8$ mol is produced; after the second step, 0.8×0.8 mol $= 0.64$ mol is produced; after the third step, 0.8×0.64 mol $= 0.512$ mol of D is produced ✓.

D is $CH_3CH(OH)COOH$ and the mass of D produced $= 90\,\text{g mol}^{-1} \times 0.512$ mol $= 46$ g ✓.

A yield of 80% means 80% by moles, not by mass.

(c) (i) $[H^+] = 10^{-pH} = 10^{-2.04} = 0.00912\,\text{mol dm}^{-3}$ ✓

$$K_a = \frac{[H^+][CH_3CH(OH)COO^-]}{[CH_3CH(OH)COOH]} = \frac{[H^+]^2}{[CH_3CH(OH)COOH]} ✓$$

$$= \frac{0.00912^2}{(0.100 - 0.00912)} = 9.15 \times 10^{-4}\,\text{mol dm}^{-3} ✓$$

Making the assumption that [acid] = 0.100 mol dm^{-3} would give the answer $K_a = 8.32 \times 10^{-4}$ mol dm^{-3} and would still score full marks. The method shown above is better because it is more accurate. Remember that in calculations about weak acids of formula HA, $[H^+] = [A^-]$. This does *not* apply to buffer solutions. You must make sure that you can use your calculator to work out $[H^+]$ from pH and K_a from pK_a.

(ii) Compound D has a larger value for K_a than does propanoic acid. Therefore, D is a stronger acid and more ionised. It would be more exothermic in its reaction with alkali than propanoic acid ✓. This is because less of the acid, D, has to be dissociated, which is an endothermic process ✓, before reaction with OH^- ions.

This can also be explained using a Hess's law cycle.

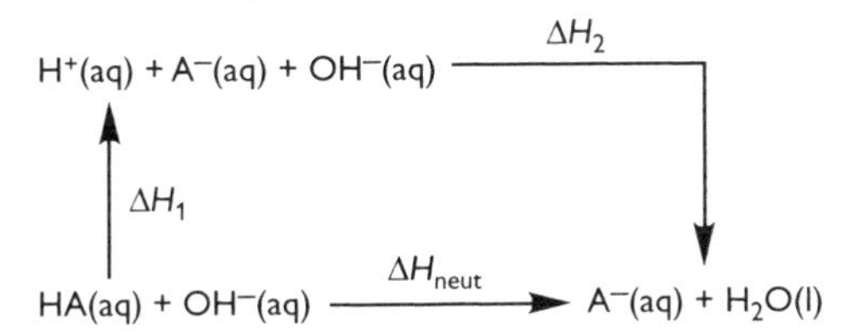

ΔH_1 = energy required to ionise the amount of acid *undissociated* in solution
ΔH_2 = energy released on neutralisation of $H^+(aq)$

$\Delta H_{neut} = \Delta H_1 + \Delta H_2$

Strong acids are totally ionised, so $\Delta H_1 = 0$. The weaker the acid, the more molecules that are undissociated and hence the more endothermic the value of ΔH_1.

Unit Test 6B, June 2002

Section A

This question is *compulsory*.

Question 1

A fertiliser is known to contain ammonium sulphate, $(NH_4)_2SO_4$, as the only ammonium salt. This question concerns methods for the determination of ammonium and sulphate ions.

(a) A sample weighing 3.80 g was dissolved in water and the volume made up to 250 cm^3. To 25.0 cm^3 portions of this solution, about 5 cm^3 (an excess) of aqueous methanal was added. The following reaction took place:

$$4NH_4^+(aq) + 6HCHO(aq) \longrightarrow C_6H_{12}N_4(aq) + 4H^+(aq) + 6H_2O(l)$$

The liberated acid was treated directly with 0.100 mol dm^{-3} aqueous sodium hydroxide. The average volume required was 28.0 cm^3. Calculate the percentage of ammonium sulphate in the fertiliser. (5 marks)

(b) In a second determination of the ammonium ion content, the same mass of fertiliser (i.e. 3.80 g) was treated with excess sodium hydroxide and heated. The ammonia liberated was passed into a known excess of hydrochloric acid. The unreacted hydrochloric acid was then titrated with standard aqueous sodium hydroxide. Calculation of the percentage composition of the fertiliser gave a value that was 5% lower than the value obtained by the method in (a). Suggest reasons for this error, other than those arising from the measurement of volume. (2 marks)

(c) To determine the sulphate ion concentration of the fertiliser, aqueous barium chloride was added in excess to the fertiliser solution. The precipitate produced was filtered off and dried by strong heating.

(i) Give the ionic equation for the precipitation reaction, including state symbols. (2 marks)

(ii) Suggest why aqueous barium chloride was added in excess. (1 mark)

(d) Many carbonates are also insoluble, and can be precipitated, dried and weighed in experiments similar to (c). However, the strong heating needed to drive off all the water can cause a problem in determining the mass of the carbonate precipitated. Suggest what this problem is, and, choosing a suitable carbonate, write an equation for a reaction that might occur when the precipitate is heated. (4 marks)

Total: 14 marks

Answer to Question 1

(a) Amount of NaOH in titration = $0.100\,mol\,dm^{-3} \times 0.0280\,dm^3 = 0.00280\,mol$ ✓
As H^+ and OH^- react in a 1:1 ratio, amount of $H^+ = 0.00280\,mol$
NH_4^+ and H^+ are also in a 1:1 ratio, so amount of $NH_4^+ = 0.00280\,mol$
1 mol $(NH_4)_2SO_4$ produces 2 mol NH_4^+, so amount of $(NH_4)_2SO_4$ in $25.0\,cm^3$ sample $= \frac{1}{2} \times 0.00280\,mol = 0.00140\,mol$ ✓
Amount of $(NH_4)_2SO_4$ in original $250\,cm^3 = 10 \times 0.00140\,mol = 0.0140\,mol$ ✓
Mass of $(NH_4)_2SO_4 = 0.0140\,mol \times 132\,g\,mol^{-1} = 1.85\,g$ ✓
% ammonium salt in fertiliser $= \frac{1.85 \times 100}{3.80} = 48.7\,\%$ ✓

Make sure that your answer shows clearly what you are calculating in each step. A common error is failing to realise that *x* moles of ammonium ions come from 0.5 *x* moles of ammonium sulphate, thus obtaining an answer of 97.4%.

(b) Some of the ammonia produced by the reaction of the ammonium ions and hydroxide ions may have remained in solution ✓. Some may have been lost by not being absorbed by the hydrochloric acid ✓ and so escaped into the air.

Suggestions such as 'handling errors' are too vague to score. The suggestion must result in a lower percentage value, which can only be caused by some ammonia being lost. The reaction between ammonium ions and hydroxide ions is complete, as sodium hydroxide was in excess. The answer 'incomplete reaction' would not gain a mark.

(c) (i) $Ba^{2+}(aq) + SO_4^{2-}(aq) \longrightarrow BaSO_4(s)$ ✓✓
(ii) Excess barium chloride is added to ensure complete precipitation of all the sulphate ions ✓.

The precipitate is barium sulphate, so the ionic equation has barium ions and sulphate ions on the left-hand side. C-grade answers might include other species in the equation. The answer 'to ensure complete reaction' is too vague for the reason for the excess barium chloride.

(d) The problem is that many carbonates decompose on heating ✓. This would result in a lower mass, as the carbon dioxide gas produced would escape ✓. An example of an insoluble carbonate that decomposes on heating is calcium carbonate ✓. The equation for its decomposition is:
$CaCO_3(s) \longrightarrow CaO(s) + CO_2(g)$ ✓

C-grade candidates might give a group 1 carbonate as their example. All group 1 carbonates are soluble and only lithium carbonate decomposes on heating. Another error might be failure to state that the mass would be lower on decomposition because a gas escaped from the system. Merely to state that carbon dioxide would be produced is not sufficient.

Section B

Answer *two* of the three questions.

Question 2

(a) The bombardier beetle *Metrius contractus* persuades potential predators to disappear by firing a boiling mixture of irritants at them. The reaction producing this ammunition is a redox reaction, H_2O_2 being the oxidising agent. The two half-reactions involved are shown in the table below.

Half-reaction	$E^{\ominus}$/V
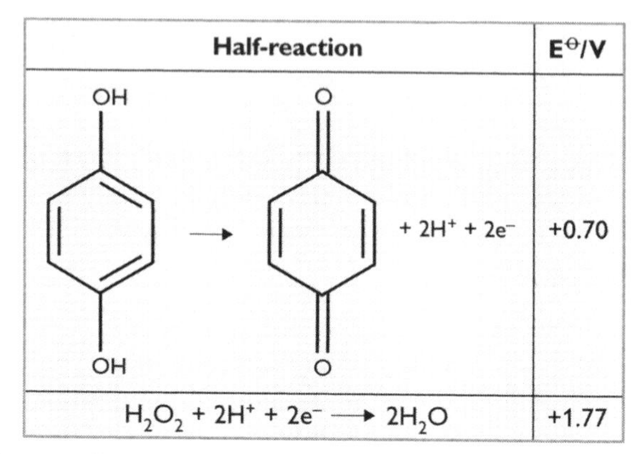 $+ 2H^+ + 2e^-$	+0.70
$H_2O_2 + 2H^+ + 2e^- \longrightarrow 2H_2O$	+1.77

(i) Write the overall equation for the reaction and show that the reaction is feasible. (3 marks)

(ii) The beetle makes use of an enzyme catalyst in this reaction. Using a graph of the Maxwell–Boltzmann distribution of molecular energies, explain, in general terms, how catalysts increase the rate of a chemical reaction. (5 marks)

(iii) The reaction is highly exothermic; in principle, its enthalpy of reaction could be found by using average bond enthalpies. By a consideration of the structure and bonding in the compounds involved, suggest why the use of average bond enthalpies for C=O, C–C, C=C and O–H would give a highly inaccurate answer for the enthalpy of reaction. (2 marks)

(b) On heating, hydrogen peroxide decomposes according to the equation

$$2H_2O_2 \longrightarrow 2H_2O + O_2$$

Hydrogen peroxide is marketed as an aqueous solution of a given 'volume strength'. The common 20-volume solution gives 20 dm^3 of oxygen from 1 dm^3 of solution. What is the concentration in $g\,dm^{-3}$ of such a solution? (Molar volume of any gas at the temperature and pressure of the experiment is 24 dm^3.) (3 marks)

(c) Hydrogen peroxide, H_2O_2, can also act as a reducing agent.
The rapid oxidation of hydrogen peroxide was used in the Second World War to generate steam to launch the V1 'flying bomb'.
H_2O_2 (100 volume) was reacted with acidified potassium manganate(VII) solution.

- **(i) Write the half-equation for the oxidation of hydrogen peroxide to oxygen, O_2.** (1 mark)
- **(ii) The MnO_4^- ions are reduced to Mn^{2+} during the reaction. Derive the overall equation for the reaction between H_2O_2 and acidified $KMnO_4$.** (2 marks)
- **(iii) Suggest in terms of the collision theory of chemical kinetics why 100-volume hydrogen peroxide (this gives 100 dm^3 of oxygen from 1 dm^3 of hydrogen peroxide when it decomposes to water and oxygen) was used rather than the more common 20-volume solution.** (2 marks)

Total: 18 marks

Answer to Question 2

(a) (i)

OH (benzene ring) OH $+ H_2O_2 \longrightarrow$ O (ring) O $+ 2H_2O$ ✓

A reaction is feasible if $E^{\ominus}_{cell}$ for the reaction is positive ✓. As the two given half-reactions are added to give the overall equation, the value of $E^{\ominus}_{cell}$ is the sum of the $E^{\ominus}$ values for the two half-reactions. In this case,

$E^{\ominus}_{cell} = +0.70 + (+1.77) = +2.47$ V ✓

which is positive, and so the reaction is feasible.

e Do not be put off by the fact that the first reaction has been written as an oxidation. This means that you must not reverse either equation. It is more common to write all the data as reduction half-equations, but it is not universal. Remember that the reactants must be on the left-hand side of the overall equation and the electrons must cancel. C-grade candidates might reverse the first equation, giving an $E^{\ominus}_{cell}$ value of +1.07 V. Another mistake might be to have the diketone on the left as a reactant, which would leave four electrons on the left of the overall equation.

(ii)

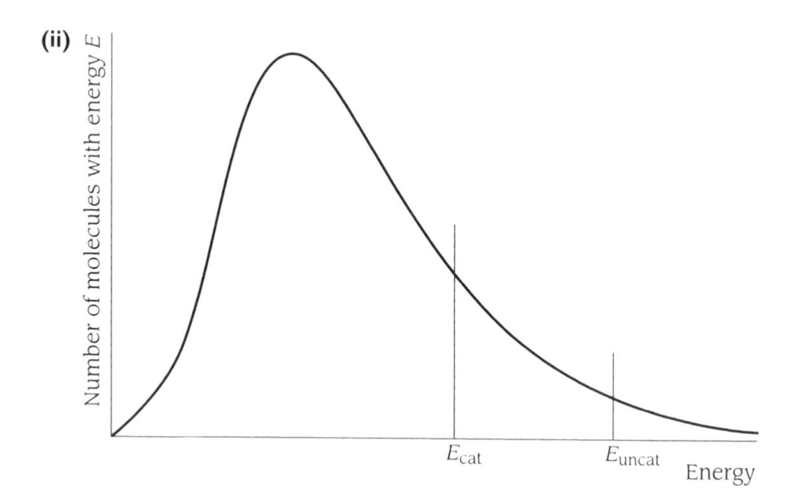

The area under the graph to the right of a particular energy, E, indicates the number of molecules with energy greater than that energy. The area under the graph to the right of E_{cat} is considerably greater than the area to the right of E_{uncat} ✓. Therefore, a much larger number of molecules will have energy greater than or equal to E_{cat} than have energy greater than or equal to E_{uncat}, and so the proportion of successful collisions will be higher in the presence of a catalyst ✓.

The marks on the graph are awarded for:

- correctly labelled axes ✓
- the correct shape ✓
- the E_{cat} and E_{uncat} being marked, both to the right of the hump ✓

Common errors on the graph would be:

- to confuse the axes
- to confuse this question with one about an increase in temperature and so draw two curves
- to mark E_{cat} to the left of the modal value (the hump)

C-grade explanations might fail to relate in detail to the graph. Expressions such as 'it can be seen from the graph that more molecules have energy greater than or equal to E_{cat} than E_{uncat}' are too vague. Specific reference must be made to areas.

(iii) The organic reactant and the organic product both have delocalised π-systems ✓. The average bond energies are the average of localised double and single bonds and so do not apply to organic compounds, such as those in this reaction ✓.

Most candidates would state that the organic substances were stabilised by resonance (or had delocalised systems), but some would fail to make it clear that average bond enthalpies do not apply to such systems.

(b) Amount of oxygen in 20 dm^3 of oxygen gas $= \dfrac{20\,dm^3}{24\,dm^3\,mol^{-1}}$

$= 0.833$ mol ✓

As 1 mol of oxygen is produced from 2 mol H_2O_2, the amount of H_2O_2 in 1 dm^3 of solution $= 2 \times 0.833$ mol $= 1.67$ mol ✓.

Concentration of H_2O_2 in g dm^{-3} $= 1.67$ mol $dm^{-3} \times 34$ g mol^{-1}

$= 56.8$ g dm^{-3} ✓

To go from mol dm^{-3} to g dm^{-3}, you must use the molar mass of H_2O_2 which is 34 g mol^{-1}, not 68. The '2' in the equation is used to convert moles of oxygen to moles of hydrogen peroxide in the second step.

(c) (i) $H_2O_2 \longrightarrow O_2 + 2H^+ + 2e^-$ ✓

Half-equations always contain electrons and must balance for charge as well as for atoms. Here both sides have a charge of zero. As the hydrogen peroxide is being oxidised, the electrons will be on the right (oxidation is loss — OILRIG). C-grade candidates might have the decomposition equation as the answer.

(ii) The half-equation for the reduction of MnO_4^- ions is:

$MnO_4^- + 8H^+ + 5e^- \longrightarrow Mn^{2+} + 4H_2O$ ✓

The overall equation is obtained by multiplying the H_2O_2 half-equation by five and adding it to two times the MnO_4^- half-equation:

$2MnO_4^- + 6H^+ + 5H_2O_2 \longrightarrow 2Mn^{2+} + 8H_2O + 5O_2$ ✓

As in (a), one equation is written as oxidation, with electrons on the right, and one as reduction, with electrons on the left. Thus there is no need to reverse either equation to get the overall equation. Note that, after addition of the two half-equations, the $10H^+$ on the right cancels with 10 of the $16H^+$ on the left.

(iii) The hydrogen peroxide is more concentrated in the 100-volume solution than in the 20-volume solution. This means that the frequency of collisions of hydrogen peroxide molecules with manganate(VII) ions will be greater ✓, and so the rate of reaction will be increased ✓.

A C-grade candidate might think that the question is about more oxygen affecting the rate. The reaction described in the stem of the question is between hydrogen peroxide and acidified potassium manganate(VII). Therefore, you have to deduce that 100-volume hydrogen peroxide is more concentrated than a 20-volume solution. Another error might be only to state that the number of collisions would be increased. 'The number of collisions in a given time increased' is a correct statement, but a better expression would refer to an increase in *the frequency of collisions*.

■ ■ ■

Question 3

Ethanol can be converted into the nitrogen-containing compounds aminoethane, $CH_3CH_2NH_2$, and ethanamide, CH_3CONH_2.

(a) The NMR spectrum of ethanol is shown below.

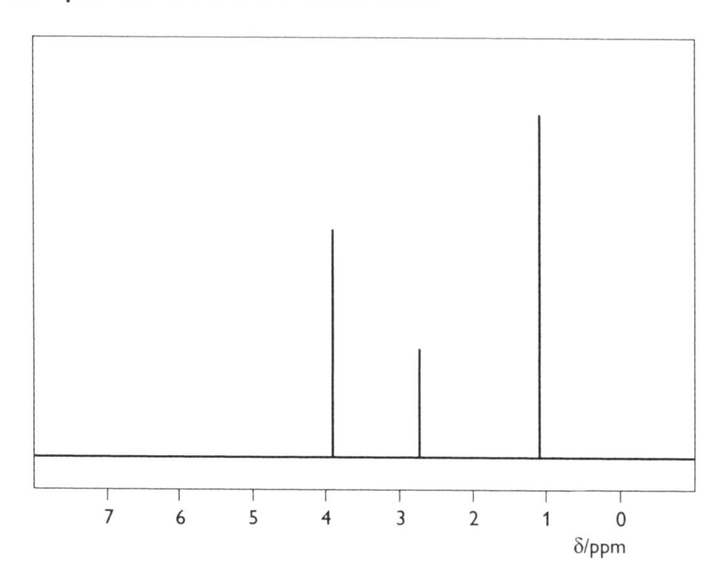

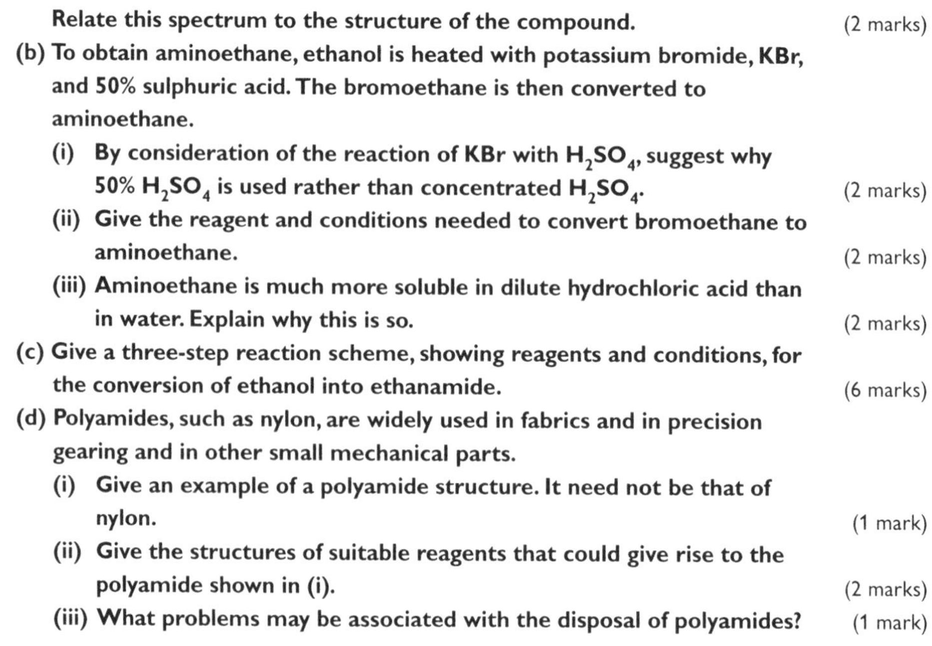

Relate this spectrum to the structure of the compound. (2 marks)

(b) To obtain aminoethane, ethanol is heated with potassium bromide, KBr, and 50% sulphuric acid. The bromoethane is then converted to aminoethane.

- **(i) By consideration of the reaction of KBr with H_2SO_4, suggest why 50% H_2SO_4 is used rather than concentrated H_2SO_4.** (2 marks)
- **(ii) Give the reagent and conditions needed to convert bromoethane to aminoethane.** (2 marks)
- **(iii) Aminoethane is much more soluble in dilute hydrochloric acid than in water. Explain why this is so.** (2 marks)

(c) Give a three-step reaction scheme, showing reagents and conditions, for the conversion of ethanol into ethanamide. (6 marks)

(d) Polyamides, such as nylon, are widely used in fabrics and in precision gearing and in other small mechanical parts.

- **(i) Give an example of a polyamide structure. It need not be that of nylon.** (1 mark)
- **(ii) Give the structures of suitable reagents that could give rise to the polyamide shown in (i).** (2 marks)
- **(iii) What problems may be associated with the disposal of polyamides?** (1 mark)

Total: 18 marks

Answer to Question 3

(a) The three peaks show that there are hydrogen atoms in three different environments. Ethanol has hydrogen atoms in three different environments ✓.

The peak heights in increasing chemical shifts are in the ratio of 3:1:2, which correspond to the three hydrogen atoms in the CH_3 in ethanol, the one hydrogen in the OH group, and the two in the CH_2 group ✓.

e The peak due to the hydrogen atom in an OH group can have a variety of chemical shifts depending on the concentration of the organic compound. In this case it is at around $\delta = 2.6$, but it can go up to $\delta = 6$. C-grade candidates often confuse nuclear magnetic resonance (NMR) spectroscopy with infrared, giving answers in terms of bonds vibrating, or with mass spectra, giving answers in terms of molecular fragmentation. NMR detects hydrogen atoms and the peak heights are proportional to the number of hydrogen atoms in each environment.

(b) (i) Use of 50% sulphuric acid produces hydrogen bromide only ✓. Concentrated sulphuric acid is an oxidising agent and so would oxidise some of the hydrogen bromide produced to bromine ✓.

e C-grade answers might suggest that the difference is due to the balanced equation having a 1:1 mole ratio, and therefore not needing as much sulphuric acid.

(ii) The reagent is ammonia ✓. The conditions involve heating the reactants in a sealed tube ✓.

e Heat under reflux is a common immediate response to a question about conditions. It cannot be correct here because the ammonia would boil off and, being a gas, would not be condensed and therefore not returned to the flask.

(iii) Aminoethane is a base and is protonated by the acid to form $CH_3CH_2NH_3^+Cl^-$ ✓. The ionic compound is more soluble than the covalent aminoethane ✓.

e C-grade answers might be confused about solubility. Many might relate the difference to the polarity of water and hydrogen chloride. In this example, the key to solubility is the protonation of the amine and the ionic nature of the product.

(c) The simplest route is:

$$CH_3CH_2OH \xrightarrow{\text{Step 1}} CH_3COOH \checkmark \xrightarrow{\text{Step 2}} CH_3COCl \checkmark \xrightarrow{\text{Step 3}} CH_3CONH_2$$

The reagents are:

Reaction	Reagents	Conditions
Step 1	Potassium dichromate(VI) and sulphuric acid ✓	Heat under reflux
Step 2	Phosphorus(V) chloride, PCl_5 ✓	Dry
Step 3	Ammonia ✓	Mix at room temperature ✓

There is 1 mark for any one correct condition. Remember to give full names or formulae for reagents. Answers such as 'acidified dichromate(VI)' or '$H^+/Cr_2O_7^{2-}$' would not score marks. When working out synthesis routes it is sometimes best to work backwards. Amides are made from acid chlorides and ammonia. Acid chlorides are made from acids, which are made by oxidising primary alcohols.

(d) (i)

$$\left(-\underset{\substack{|\\ H}}{N}-(CH_2)_6-\underset{\substack{|\\ H}}{N}-\underset{\substack{\|\\ O}}{C}-(CH_2)_4-\underset{\substack{\|\\ O}}{C}- \right)$$ ✓

Polyamides contain the peptide link, –NHCO–, and this must be drawn out in full, as in the structure above. The number of CH_2 groups could be different from those shown.

(ii) The monomers that would produce this polymer are $H_2N{-}(CH_2)_6{-}NH_2$ ✓ and $ClOC{-}(CH_2)_4COCl$ ✓.

C-grade answers might give the di-acid, $HOOC(CH_2)_4COOH$, rather than the di-acid chloride as one of the monomers.

(iii) Polyamides produce toxic fumes when burnt ✓.

An alternative answer is the potential litter problem caused by the polymer being non-biodegradable.

■ ■ ■

Question 4

(a) The first stage in the manufacture of sulphuric acid by the contact process is:

$$2SO_2(g) + O_2(g) \rightleftharpoons 2SO_3(g)$$

At 400°C, the equilibrium constant $K_p = 3.00 \times 10^4\ atm^{-1}$. A catalyst of vanadium(V) oxide is used. In a particular equilibrium mixture at 400°C, the partial pressures of sulphur dioxide and oxygen were 0.100 atm and 0.500 atm respectively. Show that the yield of SO_3 is about 95% of the equilibrium mixture. (5 marks)

(b) (i) Pure sulphuric acid is a viscous liquid with a high boiling temperature of 338°C. It has the following structure:

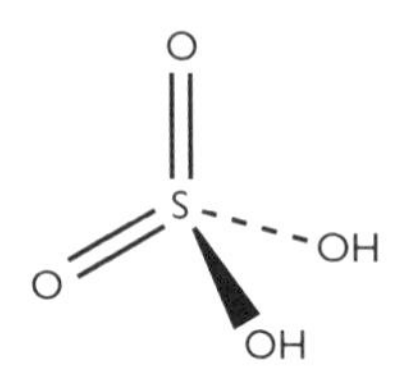

Suggest, in terms of the intermolecular forces in sulphuric acid, why it has such a high boiling temperature. (3 marks)

(ii) Sulphuric acid dissolves in water in a highly exothermic reaction.

May her rest be long and placid,
She added water to the acid;
The other girl did what we taught her,
And added acid to the water.

Suggest why sulphuric acid must always be added to water to dilute it rather than the other way round. (2 marks)

(c) Sulphuric acid dissociates in water according to the following equations:

$$H_2SO_4 + H_2O \longrightarrow H_3O^+ + HSO_4^-$$
$$HSO_4^- + H_2O \rightleftharpoons H_3O^+ + SO_4^{2-}$$

The dissociation constant for the first dissociation is very large; that for the second is 0.01 mol dm^{-3} at 25°C.

(i) Calculate the pH of an aqueous solution containing 0.200 mol dm^{-3} hydrogen ions. (1 mark)

(ii) The pH of 0.100 mol dm^{-3} sulphuric acid is 0.98. Explain why this is so close to the pH of 0.100 mol dm^{-3} HCl, which is 1.00. (3 marks)

(d) Sulphuric acid is used as the electrolyte in the lead–acid battery used in cars. The electrodes are made from lead and lead(IV) oxide. As the cell discharges, the lead and the lead(IV) oxide are both converted to lead(II) sulphate and the sulphuric acid concentration falls.

(i) Use the information above to deduce the two half-equations occurring in the lead–acid battery. (3 marks)

(ii) Hence, write an equation to represent the overall process that is taking place as the cell discharges. (1 mark)

Total: 18 marks

Answer to Question 4

(a) $K_p = \dfrac{p(SO_3)^2}{p(SO_2)^2\, p(O_2)}$ ✓ $= 3.00 \times 10^4$ atm^{-1}

$p(SO_3)^2 = K_p \times p(SO_2)^2 \times p(O_2)$ ✓ $= 3.00 \times 10^4 \times 0.100^2 \times 0.500 = 150$ atm^2

$p(SO_3) = \sqrt{150} = 12.25$ atm ✓

% of SO_3 in equilibrium mixture $= \dfrac{12.25 \times 100}{(12.25 + 0.100 + 0.500)}$ ✓

$= \dfrac{1225}{12.85} = 95\%$ (as given in the question ✓)

After realising the need to calculate the partial pressure of sulphur trioxide, the rest is fairly easy. As the partial pressure of a component is proportional to the number of moles of that substance, the percentage of sulphur trioxide equals the partial pressure of SO_3 multiplied by 100 and then divided by the sum of all the partial pressures.

(b) (i) The high value of the boiling temperature is caused by the many hydrogen bonds between molecules of H_2SO_4 ✓. These arise because both δ+ hydrogen atoms in the acid form hydrogen bonds with both very δ– oxygen atoms in the S=O groups of another acid molecule ✓. The four strong hydrogen bonds formed mean that much energy is required to separate the acid molecules and so a high boiling temperature results ✓.

C-grade candidates might be confused about which bonds are broken when a covalent liquid is boiled. It is *never* the covalent bonds. It is the intermolecular forces that have to be overcome. In this example, the forces are hydrogen bonds between sulphuric acid molecules. Another error might be to misread the question and think that the answer is about hydrogen bonds between the acid and water.

(ii) If a small amount of water is added to the acid, the heat released boils the water and a mixture of boiling water and acid is forced out by the steam ✓. If the acid is added to a large volume of water, the large volume of water absorbs the heat produced and so the mixture does not boil ✓.

You ought to know the reason as given here for the safety rule about mixing sulphuric acid and water. C-grade candidates might suggest that less heat would be evolved.

(c) (i) $pH = -\log_{10}[H^+] = -\log_{10}(0.200) = 0.70$ ✓

(ii) The first ionisation of sulphuric acid and the only ionisation of hydrochloric acid are both complete, producing the same number of hydrogen ions ✓. The second ionisation of sulphuric acid is suppressed by the H^+ ions from the first ionisation ✓ and so very few extra H^+ ions are produced. Therefore, the $[H^+]$ increases only slightly and so the pH is only a little less than the hydrochloric acid value of 1 ✓.

The question clearly shows that the first ionisation is complete ($\longrightarrow$), but the second is not ($\rightleftharpoons$). Therefore, $[H^+]$ in 0.100 mol dm^{-3} sulphuric acid is not $2 \times 0.100 = 0.200$ mol dm^{-3}, which would give a pH of 0.70. C-grade answers might fail to make the point about the suppression of the second ionisation. Poor answers might state that sulphuric acid is only slightly stronger than hydrochloric acid and therefore the pH is only slightly less. This ignores all the information about dissociation given in the question and so cannot be the answer.

(d) (i) The half-equation for the reaction at the lead electrode is:

$$Pb + H_2SO_4 \longrightarrow PbSO_4 + 2H^+ + 2e^-$$ ✓

The half-equation for the lead(IV) oxide electrode is:

$$PbO_2 + H_2SO_4 + 2H^+ + 2e^- \longrightarrow PbSO_4 + 2H_2O$$ ✓✓

You do not need to have learnt these reactions about the lead–acid battery. However, you are expected to know that they are redox reactions. All the other necessary information about the products at each electrode is given in the question. The lead is being *oxidised* to lead(II) sulphate, so there must be *two electrons* and lead(II) sulphate on the *right*-hand side of the equation. Likewise, lead(IV) oxide is being *reduced* to lead(II) sulphate, so there must be *two electrons* on the *left* and lead(II) sulphate on the right (OILRIG). The H^+ ions balance the charges in the equation. C-grade answers might give hydrogen gas as a product at the lead electrode. However, this would make it a full equation rather than a half-equation and hydrogen gas was not listed as a product in the question.

(ii) $Pb + PbO_2 + 2H_2SO_4 \longrightarrow 2PbSO_4 + 2H_2O$ ✓

e Note that the $2H^+$ on both sides cancel.

The periodic table

Key: Molar mass/g mol^{-1} / Symbol / Atomic number

Period	1	2											3	4	5	6	7	0
1	1 H 1																	4 He 2
2	7 Li 3	9 Be 4											11 B 5	12 C 6	14 N 7	16 O 8	19 F 9	20 Ne 10
3	23 Na 11	24 Mg 12											27 Al 13	28 Si 14	31 P 15	32 S 16	35.5 Cl 17	40 Ar 18
4	39 K 19	40 Ca 20	45 Sc 21	48 Ti 22	51 V 23	52 Cr 24	55 Mn 25	56 Fe 26	59 Co 27	59 Ni 28	63.5 Cu 29	65.4 Zn 30	70 Ga 31	73 Ge 32	75 As 33	79 Se 34	80 Br 35	84 Kr 36
5	85 Rb 37	88 Sr 38	89 Y 39	91 Zr 40	93 Nb 41	96 Mo 42	99 Tc 43	101 Ru 44	103 Rh 45	106 Pd 46	108 Ag 47	112 Cd 48	115 In 49	119 Sn 50	122 Sb 51	128 Te 52	127 I 53	131 Xe 54
6	133 Cs 55	137 Ba 56	139 La 57	178 Hf 72	181 Ta 73	184 W 74	186 Re 75	190 Os 76	192 Ir 77	195 Pt 78	197 Au 79	201 Hg 80	204 Tl 81	207 Pb 82	209 Bi 83	210 Po 84	210 At 85	222 Rn 86
7	223 Fr 87	226 Ra 88	227 Ac 89															

140 Ce 58	141 Pr 59	144 Nd 60	(147) Pm 61	150 Sm 62	152 Eu 63	157 Gd 64	159 Tb 65	163 Dy 66	165 Ho 67	167 Er 68	169 Tm 69	173 Yb 70	175 Lu 71
232 Th 90	(231) Pa 91	238 U 92	(237) Np 93	(242) Pu 94	(243) Am 95	(247) Cm 96	(245) Bk 97	(251) Cf 98	(254) Es 99	(253) Fm 100	(256) Md 101	(254) No 102	(257) Lr 103